HOCKMANN,
THE GREAT

EXPOSES

HIMSELF

and Other Phony
Magicians and Vaudevillians

by Milt Larsen

Illustrated by Paul Butler

Hockmann, The Great *Exposes Himself*
Published by Brookledge Corporation
7001 Franklin Avenue
Hollywood, CA 90046
323.851.3443

> With special thanks to my wife, Arlene; Chris
> Zamiara, and to the Barracuda, Carol Marie,
> who amassed all the Hockmannisms into some
> semblance of order.

Library of Congress catalog card number: 98-xxxxx
ISBN#: 0-9661005-2-2

Printed by Hignell Book Printing
488 Burnell Street
Winnipeg, MB, Canada
1.800.304.5553

Cover Design by Paul Butler
Illustrations by Paul Butler

Compiled and Overlooked
by
Carol Marie

1st Printing

THE ART OF EXPOSURE
By
Hockmann, The Great

In this book, I have revealed secrets of acts I have worked with over the past century. I am doing this exposure because I feel our craft can be improved by taking the mystery out of magic and theatrical effects. No one should withhold secrets from anyone. That goes for the government. If there were no secrets, there would be no spies and the world would be a better place to live. If Coca-Cola had no secrets, we could make the stuff in our bathtubs like in the good old days of prohibition. If Elvis had no secrets, he would be singing in Las Vegas right now.

Think of the time saved if readers found out how a story ended in the first few pages of a book. There should be capsulized reviews in the daily papers revealing the shocking twist in the last reel of the movie. People wouldn't have to wait in long theatre lines and, therefore, more theatres could be turned into churches.

I know I will be criticized for exposing many secrets in this book about the golden days of vaudeville. I figure, what the hell, I have no friends anyway. I haven't been able to get booked since World War II. And, I'm too old to have sex. I might as well expose myself.

Harry Hockmann

 # Who Is Hockmann?

No one seems to have met Harry Hockmann, except Milt Larsen. Larsen claims he visits Hockmann regularly at his impressive old ranch hidden away in the San Fernando Valley where the old Professor lives with his wife, Maude. The address of the ranch is a secret. According to Larsen, Harry Hockmann is a loner. He seldom sees people, particularly magicians whom he basically distrusts. He is known to have a drink, from time to time, and claims that alcohol sharpens his memory. After a stiff belt, Hockmann vividly remembers everything that has happened in the world of magic and vaudeville over the past century. Some people drink to forget ... Hockmann drinks to remember!

The publishers will not guarantee everything Hockmann recalls, in this book, actually happened. In fact, they will not guarantee *anything* Hockmann recalls ever happened. Moreover, maybe Hockmann never happened. But assuming that there really was a "Hockmann, The Great" show and ... Assuming there was once a beautiful assistant named "Maude" and ... Assuming there really is a Milt Larsen ... Well, let's expand our minds by sharing the wonderful world of Harry Hockmann, the world's oldest and greatest magician and vaudevillian alive.

In revealing the magical secrets that lie within these pages, Harry Hockmann may be banned from the Magic Castle™. Maude says this probably will not bother Harry since he hasn't been out of the house in twenty years! (Except to expose himself to a few neighbors.)

PUBLISHER'S NOTE:
In keeping with the idea of destroying mystery and suspense, we wanted to reveal how this book ends. Since there is no plot, all that can be said is, it ends on page 126.

Wolfgang Woofledust
Editor
Brookledge Publishing

My name is "Dai" Vernon and I am over ninety years of age. For well over the past eighty I have seen and known all the well known magicians.

I first met the wonderful Larsen family when the two sons Milt & Bill were small boys. The former has a hand in numerous ventures. Besides the famous Magic Castle & the theatre in San America he is rapidly transforming the Theatre of Variety arts into a popular attraction.

In spite of his many talents there is one thing I cannot understand about him.

He continually speaks & writes about a famous conjuror named Hockmann. When I asked, he informed me that his first name was Harry.

Who was this mysterious character? It seems very strange that I never even heard of him in the past many years.

Being fully aware of Milton's integrity, his tales about Hockmann have me truly puzzled.

Where was he from? Where did he appear? Is he still living or dead?

At any rate the most famous illusions and magical effects are the ones never actually seen, but talked about. A perfect example is the "Indian Rope trick".

Before I pass away I trust that I can really find out the truth about HARRY HOCKMANN.

CONTENTS

Rancho Hockmann

Magicians ask if they can visit Professor Harry Hockmann at Rancho Hockmann. Harry has not been cordial to magicians since he discovered a well-known magician in his illusion workshop with a camera and tape measure. The magician was so busy measuring the "gimmick" base of Harry's "Crushing a Lady With a Two Ton Safe Illusion" he didn't notice the old Professor. Hockmann denies he pulled the lever that released the safe, which could have killed the magician. Whenever he talks about the incident, Hockmann displays a sadistic smile. One house guest made a bottle of Harry's favorite 27 year-old Scotch disappear. Another magician tried to coax Harry's wife, Maude, into a compromising position in the Spirit Cabinet. So magicians are not welcome at Rancho Hockmann.

Hockmann has a limited circle of friends and an unlisted address. We can tell you the ranch is somewhere in the San Fernando Valley in California. The estate still has a private theatre, workshops, warehouses, and several bars. Part of the ranch is devoted to an orchard where Hockmann spends hours every day, working on his experiments in growing green olives with pimento centers.

His little valley community had a bit of excitement the other day when, according to Hockmann, the town's only bank was robbed by a nude gunman. The gunman was stark naked except for a ski mask over his head. He didn't get very far, though, as one of the female tellers recognized him as a former employee.

Hockmann kept the infamous ski mask and later gave it to a young man who wanted to rent some illusion props for some kind of TV special.

Early photos of Rancho Hockmann would indicate that the house was originally easy to spot. The house, today, is not quite what it used to be. The imposing tower was lost in the Sylmar earthquake of 1972 and commercial buildings now surround the area. The only clue is an old, rusting gate and a long driveway leading into a small forest of oak trees.

Hockmann (lower left) always invited an unusual group of friends to his elaborate parties at Rancho Hockmann.

Because of its towers and numerous turrets, many people in the Valley referred to Rancho Hockmann as "The Castle." In the early days, Harry would stand in front of the house for hours waiting for his fans to drop by and ask for his autograph. Actually, the alligator-filled moat kept most visitors away from the main residence.

"The Hockmann Boat Party" was held May 27, 1929, during Prohibition at Rancho Hockmann. A boat in the middle of arid San Fernando Valley? It seems Hockmann had built a man-made lake on some acreage that has now been sold off to the oil companies. (Those houses south of the Rancho look like typical Valley homes, but they are actually cleverly disguised oil wells.)

The boat that Harry kept on the Lake wasn't a fancy millionaire's yacht. It was the only stern wheeler riverboat in the Valley. The night of the party, the calliope on the top deck played, "How Dry I Am" for the arriving guests and the booze flowed like wine. Hockmann borrowed his old friend, Paul Whiteman, from the Coconut Grove to provide first class music for dancing in the grand salon of the boat. Film stars took turns doing hilarious impressions of each other. The highlight of the party, according to Maude, was when the military band onshore struck up "There'll Be a Hot Time in the Old Town Tonight" while dancing showgirls set off hundreds of skyrockets.

Somehow, the Federal Revenue Agents noticed the party and raided the boat. In an effort to get rid of the evidence, the boat's crew threw cases of illegal booze into the steam boiler, which, unfortunately, was lit at the time. It was a spectacular end to a great party and a fine boat.

In 1975, a noted astrologer predicted that the lower part of the State of California would fall into the sea as a result of a giant earthquake. Because of this, Hockmann threw a great party to celebrate the event. He figured if we were going to go, we might as well not leave any booze behind. The guests who left the Rancho the morning after said the earthquake was great. Some of the guests recalled a green and yellow polka-dot sea monster that tried to swim through the gates of Rancho Hockmann as the ocean water gushed through the floor of the San Fernando Valley. Maude said there was no water and there was no sea monsters ... and she should know because she paddled the drunken guests home in her canoe.

Lake Hockmann was one of the few private lakes in the San Fernando Valley. The quaint boat house had a few dozen guest rooms and several bars. Harry can't quite remember if the above photo was taken before his boat was launched, or after it blew up and sank.

Hockmann recently gave in to financial pressures and sold off several acres of Rancho Hockmann. One such acre was the area that housed Hockmann, The Great show's animal cages. The area was completely isolated from the outside world and was something like a jungle compound. Harry had a great view of the animals from his study window where he spends most of his time these days. Harry wouldn't disclose how much he sold the property for, however, we do know he has refused huge offers from supermarkets and developers in the past.

The new owners are the "Skinny-Dappers," an organization of sun worshipers from Arizona.

Hockmann's quaint den where Harry loves to spend cold winter nights curled up with a good bottle of gin, while roasting juniper berries over the roaring fire.

Hockmann's Age

No one knows how old the old Professor is. Harry claims to have known famous people like Alexander Graham Bell and P.T. Barnum. According to Hockmann, he lent his friend, Tom Edison, his magic flower production cone to amplify Edison's new gramophone. His vivid recollection of the San Francisco earthquake of 1906 is earthshaking. If this is true, and I have no reason to doubt his word, it would make Hockmann a very old man. To prove it, Hockmann says he has pictures around the house what were taken before the invention of photography. You can't be more honest than that!

Harry says age is a mental condition. "You're as young as you feel." And Hockmann has felt terrible for almost a century! Maude surprised us at the annual Social Security Chug-a-lug Festival by announcing that Hockmann is still great in bed. She went on to explain, "He sleeps like a baby." Harry recently bought a water bed but decided it was too hard. The next day he bought a water softener.

Hockmann, The Great was always investing in some "get rich quick" scheme. He says, some of them led to his premature aging. Professor Hockmann lost a fortune one year trying to establish an alligator shoe factory in Florida. Sadly, nobody told Harry that alligators prefer to run around in their bare feet.

Harry bought some Florida land back in the thirties which turned out to be a huge swamp. Lucky Hockmann made out like a bandit when he sold the land in the 1960's to some nut relative of Walt Disney. Harry originally paid five dollars an acre for the land and sold it for one hundred dollars an acre. That, as much as anything else, is the reason people respect Hockmann as a businessman as well as a great showman.

Mrs. Hockmann says Harry never had a problem with income taxes. He was audited in 1941. At that time, the IRS asked him to come down to their office with his old records. Hockmann walked in with a wagon load of Glenn Miller, Bing Crosby and the Hoosier Hot Shots 78's. He did some of his favorite boring card tricks for the investigator; the kind where he'd deal out the whole deck into piles of two. Then, Harry regaled the tax auditor with a series of anecdotes about his boyhood days in show business and topped it off with some family slides of his trip to Nebraska.

The IRS has never audited Harry again.

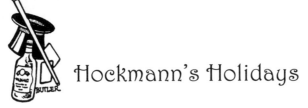 Hockmann's Holidays

Ground Hog Day

Every February, if the ground hog sticks its little head out of his winter hole and sees his shadow, it means he can go back to sleep for another six weeks. If it's cloudy, he has to get up and go to work.

According to the old Professor, magicians have their own "Ground Hog Day." In England, they refer to it as "Hare Day" from which, of course, comes the old wheeze, "Hare Today ... Gone Tomorrow." According to that old tale, or "old tail," if you prefer, if the rabbit pops its head out of the magician's top hat on February 3rd and sees his shadow on the stage, he knows the spotlight is on and his boss is working. If there is no shadow, he pops back into the hat and goes to sleep for another few weeks. He knows it may be Easter before the magician gets another gig. Magicians call that a "Bare Hare Day."

Hockmann's Hoax

Magicians are notorious for playing practical jokes on each other and Hockmann's April Fool's Day party brings out the worst in them. Guests still talk about the night W.C. Fields visited the Rancho for the 1937 April Fool's Day party. When W.C. arrived, all the guests were huddled around the radio listening to the graphic account of the Seagram's Distillery being totally destroyed by fire. The news commentator announced the distillery was gone, the fire had spread to the warehouses and the major part of the country's booze supply was going up in flames. W.C. clutched his heart and keeled over. It took a fifth of gin to bring him around. The young man who perpetuated the hoax radio broadcast of the "Great Seagram's Fire of 1937" was a magician with acting aspirations, named Orson Welles. (One year later, he did a similar hoax about Mars.)

Fourth of July

Hockmann always polished off a fifth on the 4th. Usually it was gin. In talking about magic and the Fourth of July, Harry recalled the plight of "The Great Binzetti" and his finale of producing a giant talking parrot. On the 4th of July, 1927, the parrot made the mistake of saying, "Polly want a cracker," to a group of college students playing with fireworks. One of the kids gave the bird a lit firecracker which went off in his beak. Binzetti said the parrot shot its mouth off once too often.

On the 4th of July, 1939, "Sky Rockette and his Pyrotechnic Revue" played a console that controlled banks of skyrockets, pinwheels, smoke bombs, sparklers, and cherry bombs. Sky's last performance was the old Stattsenffeffer Opera House in Michdenhoffen, Germany. At the height of Sky's performance, the Nazi Storm Troopers thought the explosions were an assassination attempt on Adolph Hitler's life and immediately leveled the theatre with mortar fire.

Mexican Magic

Professor Hockmann celebrates Cinco de Mayo by making his martinis with tequila. In sipping the potent broth, Hockmann recalled an act of his with a Mexican theme. He did the torn and restored enchilada, a switch on the "Dizzy Limit" (the Vanish of a Lady In a Net Hammock routine). Hockmann had the hammock built to look like a huge taco shell and a lady came out as a chili pepper. At the shot of a pistol, the taco shell opened and shredded lettuce fell to the stage floor. The Hot Mama had disappeared!

Harry also did a beautiful number with the old "rice bowls" using refried beans and guacamole. The latter was a trifle messy, but not nearly as sloppy as the time he forgot to produce his cute magic rabbit out of his sombrero before he went into his big Mexican Hat Dance number.

Labor Day

Professor Hockmann always has an Annual Labor Day Magic Picnic at Rancho Hockmann. It is sponsored by the National Safety Council. They feel lives can be saved by keeping Hockmann and his friends off the streets over the long weekend. Traditionally, the guests are awakened at dawn by the sound of champagne corks popping to the strains of the 1812 Overture, played by the Bartender Band. Then there are beer drinking contests and wine tastings, leading up to the cocktail hour martini championships.

The evening is devoted to a big show in Hockmann's private theatre, which may or may not actually exist. Hockmann calls it the "Delirium Tremens Revue." It features many of Hockmann's favorite "beasts of the mind."

Maude Hockmann thought Harry had finally taken his doctor's advice and given up drinking by switching to Perrier water instead of his usual straight-up martini. Hock was seen nursing a tall glass of sparkling liquid. Actually, Harry can't stand Perrier water, but he wanted to improve his image, so he found a way to carbonate gin!
(Hockmann health tip: NEVER EAT FOOD ON AN EMPTY STOMACH.)

Memorial Day

Hockmann can't quite remember what we are supposed to remember on Memorial Day, but it did jog his memory about Lucius VanSpector, who developed the great theory of memory through disassociation. For example, if he wanted to remember the serial number on a railroad boxcar, he would simply disassociate it with a hot fudge sundae.

To remember a person's name, you simply think of something like a person slipping on a banana peel. Then, when you see a person fall after slipping on a banana peel, you automatically picture that name because it has nothing to do with the incident. VanSpector could memorize an entire book through disassociation ... a ten speed bicycle has nothing to do with a field of cabbage, etc. It is truly a remarkable memory system that few people utilize today. Hockmann toasts Lucius VanSpector, "The Rajah of Recollection" every Memorial Day.

Magician's Assistant Day

Magician's Assistant Day is one day of the year set aside to honor the unsung heroes and heroines of every great magic show. It started back in the 15th century when the legendary "Marmaduke, the Magnificent" decided to amaze the King's court by sticking swords through himself while inside a box. The logistics of the illusion were impossible until Marmaduke enlisted the services of a fair maiden, Guinevere of Camelot, a lady of great beauty and little brain. Guinevere did a great job sticking the swords through the box but didn't understand the importance of timing. It was crucial to wait until "Marmaduke, the Magnificent" was in the proper position. After Marmaduke got out of the hospital, he put Guinevere in the box and the concept of the "Magician's Assistant" was born.

Friday, the 13th

If the 13th of the month happens to fall on a Friday, many people think that's a sign of bad luck. Not Hockmann. Every Friday, the 13th, Hockmann throws a party. He's been doing it for so many years, the San Fernando Valley Police Department has it on their "Things To Do" list.

The last time the 13th fell on a Friday, Hockmann got up early in the morning and purposely flaunted common superstitions. He smashed Maude's favorite mirror, walked under a ladder, spilled some salt, and waited for a black cat to cross his path.

Despite all this, the next twenty-four hours were no different than any other day at Rancho Hockmann. Maude says the microwave oven might have exploded anyway and, at that time of the year, it's not unusual to find a rattlesnake in the bathtub. Hockmann feels the fire that destroyed his warehouse probably started the day before and was smoldering for days. Thus, by this simple experiment, Harry Hockmann proved for all time that there is no such thing as bad luck on Friday, the 13th.

Professor Hockmann Exposes the Secret of

THE SHATTERING
BROKEN & RESTORED MIRROR

WATER JETS
FED BY
UNDERSTAGE
FREEZER
UNIT

FOIL
ROLLER-
BLIND

BUTLER

BROKEN AND RESTORED MIRROR

"The Great Gallstoni" made his entire living with a superstition "Theme Act," which worked on Friday, the 13th. (He starved to death at an early age!) One of his best tricks was the "Broken and Restored Mirror Illusion." This illusion consisted of a large framed mirror, which was wheeled on stage. After a few patter lines about the superstition that breaking a mirror would bring seven years of bad luck, Gallstoni would smash the mirror with a construction worker's borrowed sledgehammer. He, then, threw a magic foulard over the frame. Gallistoni continued with the rest of his act.

At the finale of his show, "The Great Gallstoni" would return to the frame, whip off the foulard, and reveal the fully restored mirror. Gallstoni gave the old Professor the secret provided Harry would carry the secret to his grave. Harry got tired of waiting to kick off and blurted the secret out after a dozen double Scotches and a beer chaser.

The Secret:

The frame was a cleverly designed freezer unit. When the cloth was placed over the frame, it triggered a fine spray from water jets, which formed a crystal clear sheet of ice in the frame in less than an hour. A roller blind of Reynolds Wrap fell directly behind the ice, completing the illusion of a silver mirror. Simple? Yes, but simplicity is the essence of perfection in prestidigitation.

The Hazy World of Hockmann

Harry Hockmann is so old he remembers the "Deland Dollar Deck" when it still cost a dollar. Now it's possible to get a Deland Dollar Deck for a dollar, but you only get ten cards instead of fifty-two.

Many non-magicians do not realize that magicians sometimes use "shaved decks" of playing cards in their tricks. It took hours to shave cards until the electric razor was invented. It was no longer necessary to lather up a whole deck of cards. The magician merely plugged in the old electric razor and the job was done!

Harry did a fabulous card trick at Rancho Hockmann at his annual Elk Roast party. Harry asked a person to choose a card from an unprepared deck. The spectator looked at the card and placed it in his pocket. Harry went to other guests in the room and each person picked one card. Hockmann held the card up and asked if it was the chosen card. As the fifty-first person did this, it became obvious that the chosen card had completely vanished from the deck. Harry then asked the first person to name the chosen card. This done, Harry asks the first person to look in their pocket and find the card. Wow!

Bold, yes, but it works every time. The secret is, of course, by the time the fifty-first person picks the card and asks the question, the audience has totally forgotten what the trick was about in the first place. Another great Hockmann miracle!!!

Race Car Hoax

America's first automobile race was held September 28th, 1895. It was a race between six cars on a fifty-five mile course. The winner, Frank Duryea, made it in record time ... seven hours, fifty-three minutes!

Harry Hockmann tells of the "Great Motor Car Race Hoax of 1912." This was a race between ten bitter rivals with a $50,000 grand prize to the victor.

Nine of the entries were fabulous cars in brilliant brass and polished lacquer. They were tremendously expensive machines and "state of the art" for 1912.

One entry, "The Banger Eight," was named after its designer and driver, Homer P. Banger. The Banger Eight was a runt of a car, obviously put together with the cheapest spare parts. The other drivers laughed and scoffed when Homer drove it up to the starting line.

The flag was up and the race was off ... with Homer clearly lost in the dust. Near the end of the race the cars roared through a long tunnel before the last mile to the finish line. The crowd cheered in disbelief as Homer's Banger Eight came roaring out of the tunnel to win the race, and the $50,000! The secret was later revealed. Homer had built two identical cars. He simply hid one after the other racers passed him and phoned ahead to his identical twin brother parked in the darkness at the end of the tunnel.

Ice Sculpture

In 1929, Harry took the entire profits from his very successful "Prestidigipulchritude Revue of 1928" and invested the money in a sure-fire attraction. The world's most famous ice sculptor, Izzadore Chitzelmeyer, spent ten years creating a scale model of the city of London out of a huge block of solid ice.

Hockmann bought the famous ice masterpiece in England and had it shipped to his Rancho Hockmann. He had it mounted on a large flatbed truck and planned to tour United States with the ice sculpture, beginning in Los Angeles on the 28th of August, 1929.

Unfortunately, that date turned out to be unseasonably hot with a temperature of 110 degrees. The unveiling was less than a big success. Hockmann recouped a few dollars of his loss through the sale of freshly melted spring water. Luckily, Hockmann had most of his money in stocks and bonds and looked forward to the continued prosperity of 1929 and the coming thirties.

AMAZING STONEWALL

The amazing "Stonewall, The Sorcerer," was a music hall performer in England around the turn-of-the-century. Stonewall would invite a committee of stone masons on stage where a cement mixer was churning a load of fast-setting mortar. Each mason was given an ordinary, unprepared trowel and assigned the task of building a wall of quarry stone, six feet wide by eight feet tall by nine inches thick. Then, the tall, handsome Sidney Stonewall would put on a pointy crash helmet and allow himself to be stuffed into the mouth of a British Naval cannon. One of the Queen's marksmen would take careful air at the center of the stone wall and fire. Blam!!! When the smoke cleared away, "Stonewall, the Sorcerer" could be seen bowing on the other side of the wall! It was a great illusion. (It is sad to report that, one night, his elaborate set of trap doors failed to operate and he really was shot from the cannon. He became known thereafter as "Shorty, the Silly Sorcerer"!)

Hockmann's Autographs

Hockmann has an amazing autograph book in his personal archives. Some of the names are fantastic. Movie star autographs include Francis X. Bushmann, Clark Gable, Burt Reynolds, and Minnie Mouse. Harry has each and every President of the United States dating back to William McKinley. His collection contains personal inscriptions to Hockmann from the inventors like Alexander Graham Bell and Thomas Edison! In fact, when this biographer questioned the Professor about some of the early names being signed with a ball point pen, Hockmann quickly pointed out the ball point pen was a new invention of Edison's. Unbelievable, but true.

In discussing the Hancock signature on the Declaration of Independence, the subject came up of signatures and forgeries. Harry, it seems, was most concerned over the possibility of a forgery in the matter of Howard Hughes' "Mormon Will." Hockmann made a new will and, to thwart would-be forgers, Harry refused to sign it! An old crony of Hockmann's, "Banker Bunny" McGee, was known as "The Magician of the Moniker." McGee's greatest triumph was signing the warden's name on his own release. He went on to invent a machine that would revolutionize the art of forgery. Unfortunately, there was not a large market for a "forging machine." Ironically, a group of industrialists took the idea several years later and made a fortune with it. Benny called his invention "Forge-o-Matic," the industrialists called theirs: "Xerox"!

Tom Mix & His Horse

Harry reminisces about the time the famous cowboy star, Tom Mix, visited Rancho Hockmann. When Maude answered the doorbell, Tom Mix entered the house riding his famous white stallion, "Tony." Hockmann said he wasn't surprised to find a huge horse in his living room because he had seen many strange animals in his house before. One, he recalled, was a purple elephant with a pink striped boa constrictor as a trunk. Another was a bright red mud turtle that amused Hockmann by doing tricky handstands and back flips. Maude always said, "As long as Harry has his bottle, we'll never need pets."

Stanley & Livingston

One of Harry's favorite films of all time was "Stanley and Livingston" with Spencer Tracy. After the film came out in the thirties, Hockmann created a new illusion based on the film. In Hockmann's version, Dr. Livingston ran into a phone booth to call Stanley as a bunch of natives threw spears through the walls of the phone booth, (a clever switch on the old "Sword Box" routine). The audience never quite accepted the illusion. (Since Alexander Bell didn't get his patent on the telephone until 1876 and Stanley found Livingston in 1871, there may have been a slight historical believability gap.)

Wizard of Oz

Professor Hockmann recalls a magician who used to work the midwest called "The Great Zammo, the Wizard of Oz." The Frank L. Baum estate got after him and he was forced to change his name to "The Great Whappo, the Wizard of Oz." Whappo did a great transposition illusion wherein the Tin Man ended up being the Cowardly Lion. The Cowardly Lion turned out to be Dorothy. Dorothy turned out to be the Straw Man. The Straw Man turned out to be Toto, the dog. The dog turned out to be the Wizard of Oz. Hockmann recalled all this while he sipped champagne from one of the original ruby slippers he found under an old house set at the MGM Studio auction. At the time, MGM claimed they only had one pair which they auctioned off for a fortune. The guards did not notice Hockmann wearing the ruby slippers as he walked off the back lot.

Will Rogers

Harry was doing a benefit in Hollywood a few months before the beloved humorist, Will Rogers, met his untimely death in a plane crash. Roger was in the audience when Hockmann invited him on stage to be part of Harry's pickpocket act. After Harry had taken Will's belt (which caused his pants to fall), Harry yanked off Will's shirt, and handed Will his watch and wallet. Will Rogers rescinded his most famous line: "I never met a man I didn't like."

Professor Hockmann Exposes the Secret of

The New and Improved No-Skill
DOUBLE LIFT

"Skill is unnecessary
if you know a good
surgeon!"
— Hockmann'99

IMPLANTED MAGNETS
IN FINGERS

STEEL
CARD

REMAINDER
OF DECK

BUTLER

DOUBLE LIFT

What is a double lift? In England, a double lift is two elevators! To a hitchhiker, it's a lucky day! To an average woman, it's a brassiere! But to the magician, a double lift is a very clever move wherein two cards are taken off the top of the deck as if they were one.

The Secret:

The double lift is accomplished by having the second card in the deck made out of very thin metal and painted to look like your average linen card. The magician, then, undergoes a minor operation in which tiny magnets are inserted into his fingers. This can be done right in the doctor's office and even your best friends need not know about it. The magnetic fingers are very useful for many other standard effects as well, however, magicians must be cautioned not to edit magnetic tapes, handle computer floppy disks, or ATM and credit cards. And, if you have a pacemaker, do not salute the flag!

PACKING BOX ESCAPE

Few people remember that, like Houdini, Professor Harry Hockmann also played a magical detective in the early days of Hollywood. Harry was a crime buster "Cliff Hangre" in a series of serious serials designed to keep you clutching your seat at the Bijou. Harry would escape from the path of speeding locomotives and spectacular avalanches of sponge rubber rocks. The only thing Hockmann couldn't escape from was the escape clause in his studio contract.

Hockmann had an "escape trick." It was the large trunk he would get into, after he called the freight line to pick up his luggage at the hotel. Most of the hotel owners were on to Hockmann's trick and made Harry pay in advance, before he "vanished."

Hockmann recalls a famed theatrical hotel in Boston in the thirties where the owner didn't trust vaudevillians. He always made them leave part of their act as a deposit. Hockmann left his vanishing horse. The horse left a deposit of his own minutes before it vanished!

Fires

Mrs. O'Leary's cow kicked over a lantern in 1871 and started the disastrous Chicago Fire. This disaster so moved young Thomas Alva Edison that he started work on inventing the electric light. A few years later Mrs. O'Leary's cow ate through an electrical wire which started a fire in her new barn. Luckily, in this case, the Chicago firemen contained the fire to the barn and her cow.

Many residents of the San Fernando Valley still remember the Great Fire of 1928. This started when Hockmann's trained goat kicked over a bottle of volatile prohibition booze at a barn party. Fortunately, in 1928, there was very little to burn down in the San Fernando Valley. The Chicago Fire of 1871 destroyed 17,000 buildings. The Great Fire of the San Fernando Valley got an old movie set and three chicken coops.

The Great Depression

"The Great Depression" started in 1929. When asked if Hockmann remembered it, Harry said he thought it was the stage name of a pretty sad illusionist out of Detroit. Hockmann wasn't bothered too much by the depression. He went broke in the boom! Hockmann admits he is not clever in his business dealings. He invested in the Cape Canaveral Retirement Village, the San Andreas Fault Towers, the 120 r.p.m "short-playing" phonograph record, and invigorating California Ice Tubs for health spas. Hockmann's show actually did well during the Depression because nobody could afford to go to a really good show.

The Great Draught of 1937

"The Great Draught of 1937" in the San Fernando Valley went on for almost half a year before Hockmann knew about it. The reason is because very little water is consumed at Rancho Hockmann. (Harry always kept an Arrowhead Spring water dispenser at the ranch for show, but it was filled with Vodka.)

"The Great Draught of '37" ended with the "Great Flood of 1938" which ended with "The Great Earthquake of 1939." Of all the natural disasters, Hockmann says he likes earthquakes best. According to the old Professor, that's the only time the floor stops moving.

Famous Greats

In the year 1666, "The Great Fire of London" destroyed 13,000 houses, 89 churches and, according to our historian Harry Hockmann, 427 pubs. A few years later, in 1871, Mrs. O'Leary's cow knocked over a lantern in her barn and started "The Great Chicago Fire." Then there was "The Great Fire and Earthquake" in San Francisco in 1906. In 1929, we entered "The Great Depression." Why do they always refer to these disasters with the phrase "The Great"? What's so great about a disaster? This question was raised by "Hockmann, The Great" who has been responsible for some of the greatest theatrical disasters of all time.

Al Capone

"Ten Nights in a Barroom," the famous temperance melodrama, opened in New York at the National Theatre in 1879. Hockmann used the play as a basis for a magical sketch in his "Great Hockmann Show of 1926." Harry called his version "Ten Days in a London Pub" and magically produced gallons of beer from empty kegs, bottles, and booze from every conceivable place. The beer was genuine and so was the concern of the revenue officers since prohibition was in full effect in 1926. After the show was closed in a raid. Hockmann lost the financial support of one of his principal patrons of the arts, Mr. Al Capone of Chicago.

Hockmann claims the famed racketeer, Al Capone, wasn't really a bad guy. He was trying to do what he thought was right ... giving the American people what they wanted: booze! Apparently Capone was a magician in his own right. (Think of the number of people he made disappear.) Hockmann also reminds us that Sid Grauman stole an idea from Capone for his Grauman's Chinese Theater in Hollywood. It was Al Capone who originally put footprints in concrete!

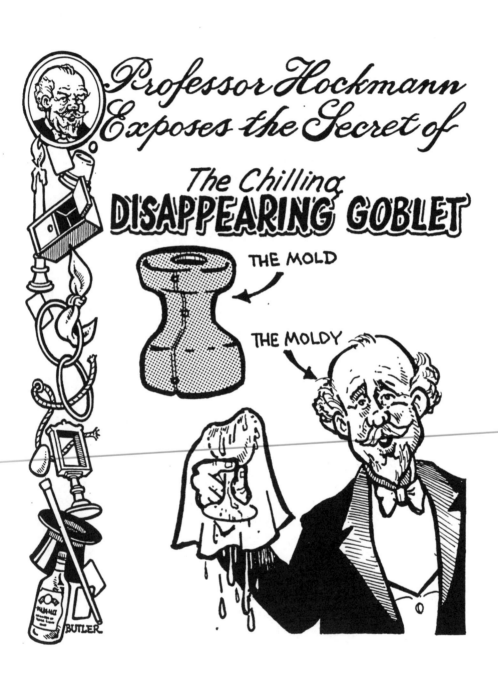

Professor Hockmann Exposes the Secret of

The Chilling DISAPPEARING GOBLET

THE MOLD

THE MOLDY

DISAPPEARING GOBLET TRICK

"The Disappearing Goblet Trick" is one of the most beautiful effects in magic. A large crystal goblet is shown to the audience, then filled with water. It is covered with a borrowed handkerchief. Slowly the hanky is seen getting wet and the form of the goblet sinks beneath the hanky until it is no more. The soggy hanky is removed and given back to the spectator. The glass has disappeared, leaving only a puddle of water! A miracle!

The Secret:

Make a rubber mold of a crystal goblet. Fill the mold with spring water and place it in the freezer. When frozen, it is an exact duplicate of the goblet ... in ice! The rest of the trick works itself. The goblet is shown, placed on the table and filled with lukewarm water. (This looks like cold water.) It is then immediately covered with the hanky. The lukewarm water will melt the ice so the glass appears to slowly vanish. The audience cannot tell there is more water on the table than what was poured into the goblet. It's a real baffler.

HOT TIP: If you want to speed up the trick, use hot water.

Mickey Mouse vs. Rodney Rat

The first animated cartoon featuring Mickey Mouse was "Steamboat Willie" which opened at the Colony Theater in New York in 1928. The old Professor claimed Walt Disney stole the mouse character from him.

Hockmann used a rodent in his act long before 1928 instead of a rabbit. Some of the tricks were "Gloves to Rat," "The Hong Kong Rat Vanish," and, of course, the old "Rat Out of the Hat Trick." Unfortunately, this was the year Hockmann introduced his "Passe-Passe Rattlesnake" trick. One night the assistants put Rodney Rat in the same cage as Ralph Rattlesnake. Hockmann didn't replace Rodney Rat because of the instant popularity of Mickey Mouse. Hockmann still thinks he might have gotten the edge on Disney if only he had thought to dress Rodney in little red shorts with big white buttons. (That's show biz.)

Firebowl Effect

The only time Hockmann was mugged was when he made the mistake of taking a short-cut through a dark alley in New York City. A couple of guys jumped him and ran off with a package containing a large production "flash bowl" Hockmann used in the opening of his show. Hockmann was taking it to the magic shop for repairs since it kept bursting into flames prematurely. Less then three hours after the bowl was stolen, he got a call from the New York Fire Department saying they had located the prop after putting out a blaze at the Ajax Pawn Shop. Hockmann still uses the device to light his barbecue at Rancho Hockmann.

Dance Steps ala Hockmann

In 1938, one of the great dance partners of the stage died in a plane accident while instructing British pilots during World War II. He was Vernon Castle of the famous dance team, "Vernon and Irene Castle." In those days, every ballroom dancer was doing "The Castle Walk." These days, the Castle Walk is a path used by magicians sneaking past the parking attendant at Hollywood's Magic Castle.

Many people do not realize that Harry Hockmann invented a popular dance step of the twenties. It was later called the "Shimmy" but it all started when Hockmann was doing his popular barehanded production of live rats and his rat-dropper broke. Maude Hockmann added that the Shimmy wasn't the only new dance step Harry invented that night.

Critic's Choice

"The Great Hockmann Show" was reviewed in The New York Times after the opening of his new show in 1938. That was also the year Hockmann canceled his subscription to the Times. It is interesting to note that Hockmann used a quote from that review for the next several seasons. The quote was "Hockmann, The Great ... the greatest thing that could happen to magic!" The actual review said: "If only the Great Hockmann would get out of show business it would be the greatest thing that could happen to magic!"

BARE STAGE REVIEW

"Our Town," a play by Thornton Wilder, opened at the Henry Miller Theater in New York in 1938. The play was quite unusual in that it used a bare stage as its setting. A few months after it opened, it won the Pulitzer Prize, which Hockmann resented.

Hockmann claims his extravagant "Presto Pompom Revue" of 1929 was the first show to perform on a bare stage. He cleverly opened Halloween week and the glowing notices hit the papers on October 29, 1929. Unfortunately, the news of his show was somewhat obscured by the headlines pertaining to the stock market crash. During the next few weeks, all of the props and scenery in the production were repossessed and Hockmann did the entire show with a deck of cards on a bare stage. He still swears that Thornton Wilder was in the audience and stole the "bare stage" idea for "Our Town"... The Pulitzer Prize should rightly have gone to Harry Hockmann!

Maude Hockmann & Women's Rights

Feminist Amelia Bloomer was born in 1818 and a year later, on the same date, woman suffrage leader Julia Ward Howe was born.

Women finally got the right to vote in 1920 as the Secretary of State declared the 19th Amendment operative. Maude Hockmann claims she was only a child at the time, but she remembers the celebration well. When the news was announced, thousands of ladies in Times Square threw their ballots, bustles, and brassieres in the air. For years Maude thought a "suffragette" was a magician's assistant who zigged when she should have zagged!

Never get into an argument with Maude Hockmann about the possibility of a woman president. She thinks the woman's place is in the home and that home happens to be the White House. Maude was an advocate of Women's lib long before other women started thinking about it. For instance, when "The Great Hockmann Show" was in its prime in the 20's and 30's, at Mrs. Hockmann's insistence, the printed programs read: "Sawing a Person in Half" - "The Levitation of Ms. Karnac" - and "Featuring a Chorus of Fifty - count 'em - Fifty Beautiful Persons." Of course, Hockmann's ability to save money on the wardrobe meant there was really no problem in separating the men from the girls. Hockmann would have been booked for fifty-two straight weeks in Florenz Ziegfeld's Follies if it hadn't been for Maude's fighting with Flo to change his slogan from "Glorifying the American Girl" to "Glorifying the American Person."

"The Great Hockmann," always an innovator in magic, designed a show he thought would please feminists in the 1930's. His entire cast of beautiful assistants were costumed in modest business suits, no makeup, tied back hair and flat shoes. After a sensational opening in Boston, the show died an unglamorous death in New York where it played across the street from Minsky's Burlesque.

World War II

"The Great Hockmann Show" was very popular with the troops during World War II. Hockmann wisely staged his show to feature his all-girl cast with a great deal of audience participation. According to Hockmann, he was the most decorated performer of the war. Maude adds that he probably was the most decorated ... if you include Hawaiian leis, paper party hats, and body painting. During the war, Rancho Hockmann was used as a command post in the San Fernando Valley. Civil Defense officers agreed it was the one place in Southern California that the enemy would never think of bombing. Hockmann still has some grim reminders of the war-torn days of the 1940's, an airplane spotter's wheel, some ration stamps, and a size 50 "zuit suit."

Accordion

In 1856, the first patent for an "accordion" was issued. The inventor, A.C. Cordion, took the idea of the old Bavarian concertina and added a piano keyboard. He later changed the keyboard from eighty-eight keys to twenty-four. That revision made the accordion lighter and easier to strap to the chest.

"The Great Hockmann Show of 1925" featured Harry's wife, Maude, playing the accordion while Hockmann escaped from an underwater torture cell, ala Harry Houdini. Hockmann felt rather silly doing the escape. He wore only his flesh-colored jock strap, the current rage ever since Houdini made his sensational escape after being locked nude in the Brooklyn Jail. It's interesting to note that Maude was tossed in the same jail after adding the touch of playing the accordion nude during the act. She still remembers it as a most embarrassing and painful experience.

When the final Honor Roll of Escape Artists is written, Hockmann's name will be just above Houdini — in alphabetical order, of course!

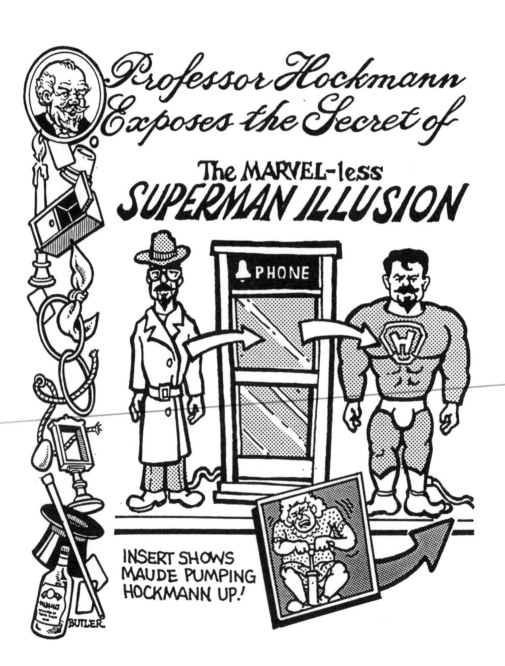

Professor Hockmann Exposes the Secret of

The MARVEL-less SUPERMAN ILLUSION

PHONE

INSERT SHOWS MAUDE PUMPING HOCKMANN UP!

BUTLER

SUPERMAN TRANSITION ILLUSION

Hockmann had a clever illusion based on a telephone booth and the popularity of Superman. It was called "The Vanish of Clark Kent in the Telephone Booth Illusion." Skinny little Hockmann put on his trench coat, glasses and a Clark Kent hat. Then Hockmann stepped into the telephone booth. The assistants closed the door for a few moments and suddenly, Superman, with bulging biceps, emerged from the booth. Hockmann, then, tore apart the booth with his bare hands to show that Clark Kent had disappeared! Superman whipped off his mask and, to the amazement of the stunned audience, Superman was revealed to be Hockmann.

The Secret:

An inflatable Superman muscle suit was hidden inside the Clark Kent trench coat. A nearly invisible air hose led offstage to Maude Hockmann and a bicycle pump. The Clark Kent suit is cleverly mixed in with the phone booth debris and easily dismissed by audiences as "trash."

Magic Silk Parachute

On March 12, 1912, Captain Albert Berry performed the first successful parachute jump from a plane! The first unsuccessful parachute jump was made by our own Professor Hockmann one year earlier from a hot air balloon over the Owhatabunchuvoosee Swamp in Florida. He had been doing the upside-down straight jacket escape over a crowd of 10,000 cheering spectators in Shreveport when the ropes holding the balloon broke and he sailed away.

Luckily, the Professor's wife, Maude, had fabricated a large "parachute" out of Hockmann's old "serpent silk trick" props. (For the layman, that's the trick where the silk scarf mysteriously unties itself.) After "Hockmann,The Great" escaped from the straight jacket, he made the first successful parachute jump as the silk untied itself mysteriously and he plunged into the swamp. (He might have been killed if he had not landed on the back of a sleeping alligator who dragged him to safety.)

Woofle Dust

Many magicians use a product called "woofle dust" in their acts. According to song and story, if a magician sees his shadow on the "First Day of Woofle" it will cause water to fall from the heavens. If it does not rain, it means magicians will have plenty of "woofle dust" for the summer. Maude Hockmann tells of the time Baby Benny Bartok put itching powder in Hockmann's woofle dust pocket. (Baby Benny was full of tricks like that.) One day, he glued the shell on Harry's billiard ball trick.

Then there was the time Hockmann ripped the sleeve off his best tail coat after Benny welded together his vanishing bird cage. Baby Benny was a million laughs, playing practical jokes even as an adult. His last job was as an assistant to the late 'Willie, the Wizard." Unfortunately for Willie, Benny was in charge of switching the real bullets for blanks in the "Bullet Catching Trick."

Vanishing Water Buffalo Illusion

The famed Hippodrome Theater in New York opened in 1905. This was the huge stage on which Harry Houdini vanished an elephant. Harry Hockmann saw Houdini do the trick and "borrowed" the idea for his own show. Instead of an elephant, Hockmann used a 7,000 pound water buffalo. The framework contraption he used to vanish the beast was made of surplus railroad track and weighed another two tons.

Everything probably would have worked out fine, even on the termite-ridden stage of the Mexicali Opera House, if it hadn't been for Maude Hockmann who did the Mexican Hat Dance just before the vanish of the water buffalo. Maude was slightly overweight at the time, due to her nervous habit of trying to lose a few pounds with her miracle diet of spaghetti and whipped cream. Maude didn't lose any weight, but Hockmann lost the water buffalo, the two ton rigging and his contract for the rest of the vaudeville season of 1906.

Kaiser's Karnival

When President Woodrow Wilson signed a proclamation of war against Germany on April 6, 1917, it was the same day that Professor Hockmann opened his new Broadway magical stage revue, "The Kaiser's Karnival of Konjuror's Revue of 1917." The Revue featured Wolfgang Von Stumph and his "Original Bund-Bogglers" troupe, the Katzenhammer Kids in "Mysteries das Militerie" and "Sigmund's Sauerbraten Sorcery." For some reason, the show was not an immediate success. (Hockmann blamed the lack of response on the fact the reviews of his show were obscured by the world war news of the day.)

Parachute Jump

Harry Hockmann was the first person to fly an airplane in Australia. Hockmann's wife recalls that Harry once jumped out of a plane without a parachute! He had consumed several double martinis at the time and landed on the ground without a scratch. (It helped that the aircraft was still on the runway at the time.)

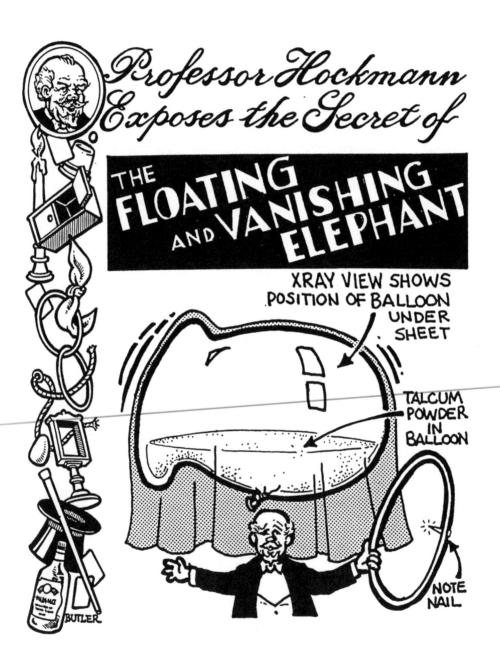

THE FLOATING & VANISHING ELEPHANT

In 1914, the first successful telephone conversation took place between two people on the Atlantic and the Pacific coasts. Hockmann reached out and touched someone in 1914, too. He got an angel to put up enough money for a sensational new illusion for his show. It was called the "Floating and Vanishing Elephant" trick. The effect was sensational. A gigantic African elephant was led on stage by uniformed elephant wranglers. Then the beast was hypnotized by Hockmann.

After covering the elephant with a huge sheet, the mammoth animal would majestically rise in the air. When Hockmann whipped away the sheet, the elephant was gone! It was a new twist on the old Asrah Levitation principle. Later, he improved on the effect by having the elephant rise in the air and vanish with a bang and a cloud of smoke.

The Secret:

Hockmann switched the live elephant for a helium-filled balloon in the shape of the elephant. In passing a twenty foot hoop over the beast, he stuck a pin in the balloon, causing it to burst with a bang. The explosion released a barrel of talcum powder inside, which created the smoke effect. Again, some of the best tricks are the simple ones.

Note: *Harry has been checking the proofs of this book and I feel the following letter speaks for itself: "Dear Milt, I read with interest the account of the Elephant Illusion. You forgot one very important part. Great care must be given to the proper training of the beast. The trick will not work with your average Hertz Rent-A-Pachyderm! The easiest way to get a really well-trained elephant is to steal one from your local traveling circus. If this is not possible, train your own very much as you would your pet doggie. Elephants will perform simple tricks on command if you give them a little treat after each trick. (A pocket full of cabbages is great for this.) Stand, fetch, sit, beg ... all these simple tricks look very spectacular on the stage when done by an African Elephant. A word of caution: When teaching the mammoth beast to "roll over and play dead," be sure to give the command on the opposite side from the direction in which you want him to roll! That's about it. Everyone out here at Rancho Hockmann sends regards, especially my old wife, Maude. Your friend, Hock.*

Standing Ovations

In 1743, King George II, rose to his feet upon hearing the Hallelujah Chorus in London. The audience rose too, giving us the first "Standing Ovation." When asked about standing ovations, the old Professor recalled the first one he ever experienced as a performer. It happened at the Furstmeyer Palace Theater in Crandall, Ohio. Hockmann had finished his original and amazing "Vanish of the Girl on Roller Skates Illusion." A lady in the audience screamed and jumped to her feet. Soon the entire audience was standing. It was an electrifying moment for Hockmann. (Maude told him later that the lady stood and screamed as a result of a large mouse climbing out of the air vent under her seat. Great showman that he is, Hockmann carried that mouse with him on the rest of his tour.)

HOCKMANN'S COHORTS

Cubernicus

Copernicus (Nikkola Kopernik), the famous astronomer, was born in 1473, at Torun, Poland. When Copernicus turned nineteen, he turned on the news and heard that Columbus had discovered America. This proved to many, the world was round; a fact many astronomers had suspected for some time. None of their telescopes showed any square or flat-shaped planets. One astronomer discovered a new twin planet which he named "Cubernicus" because it was shaped like two cubes. Later, he found a tiny pair of dice stuck to his telescope lens.

Great Bell of Silence

"The Great Bell of Silence" in Italy was unveiled in the year 1576. Every year, up to that time, the villagers of the small town of Piastiolia were awakened Sunday mornings by the ringing of the great church bell. One villager suffered from insomnia and would invariably doze off to the happy slumber land as the great bell began to toll. One morning, the villager couldn't stand it any longer and jumped on the giant swinging clapper of the bell. That morning all the villagers overslept. They were so thankful for the peace and quiet they buried the insomniac with the giant clapper. On the anniversary of the villager's death, the townspeople gather at the Cathedral and revel in the silence of the clapperless bell.

Professor Hockmann Exposes the Secret of

The Scandinavian Sorcerer

The Wizard of Nordskrog!

X-RAY VIEW OF THE ASSISTANT PRIOR TO HER VANISH

Nordskrog's firey final Finale'

BUTLER

THE SCANDINAVIAN SORCERER

The Wizard Nordskrog is still living in the small Norwegian community of Nordskrog between the California cities of Solvang and Buellton. Every year, the townspeople celebrate the Nordskrog Feather Festival (feathers being their principal industry). The festival is climaxed with a big variety show featuring the Wizard of Nordskrog. Hockmann was very impressed with the Wizard's "Vanish of a Pretty Girl in a Sleeping Bag Illusion." The pretty girl dances on stage and crawls into a common ordinary sleeping bag. The Wizard makes a pass at the girl and then picks up the sleeping bag, and turns it inside out to show that it is empty.

The Secret:

Although the illusion completely fools the layman, magicians will recognize the principle immediately. The hardest part of the trick, according to Hockmann, is getting particularly agile assistants ... especially if you plan to turn the bag inside out more than once. (This would leave Maude out of the running). The rest of the Wizard's show included his very spectacular finale which was a switch on the Great Dante's "Fountain" water fountain act, "Flames of the Wizard." The Wizard substituted lighter fluid for the usual water. The trick has also been referred to as "The Great Nordskrog High School Auditorium Disaster."

Egg Bagg

This classic magic effect was invented in 1785 by the famed English magician, Eggbert Bagg, with the help of a chicken named Chesney. The first egg bag was made of wood. Bagg quickly switched to cloth because it broke less eggs and was easier on his fingers when he turned the bag inside out. Every magician has at least two egg bags; one that he doesn't use in his act because everybody else does and one that's too soiled to use because he keeps practicing with real eggs. Hockmann featured a large stage version with a potato sack and an ostrich egg. (The audience provided quite a few eggs of their own.)

Rice Bowls

The famous Chinese magician, Long Tack Tom, invented the classic "Rice Bowl Trick" in 1788. It is interesting to note that the effect didn't go over well when he first performed it. It was several years later that magicians started including it in their repertoires. Maude thinks the problem was in Long Tack Tom's insistence on using cooked rice in the rice bowls. Later, the use of dry, uncooked rice made the trick somewhat less messy. Mrs. Long Tack Tom was fond of using the rice, after each performance, in her favorite rice pudding recipe. Maude found a copy of that recipe and has given us permission to reprint it: **Rice Pudding ala Long Tack Tom.** First, cook the rice. Pour in equal parts of soy sauce, water chestnuts and Chinese hot mustard. Whip in a wok. ("People who live in Chinese glass houses shouldn't throw woks," Maude quipped.) Pour into individual custard cups and serve.

Floating Float

Harry's uncle, "The Great Slobbo," invented the now classic floating ball. It came about as an accident. Slobbo was playing the old Trivoli Opera House in Johnstown, Pennsylvania, before the flood hit. That night, he not only invented the floating ball, but the floating piano, the floating chairs, the floating scenery! (The only thing Slobbo couldn't float was a loan.)

ʎxlɐ, and his Magic ʎx

A marvelous act on the Gun Sun vaudeville circuit, out of Chicago, was a novelty magician billed as: "Axle, and his Magic Ax." The muscular young magician would enter dressed as one of Siegfried's soldiers carrying a razor-sharp battle ax. After proving the authenticity and sharpness of the ax by chopping up celery, carrots, heads of cabbages and two-by-fours, he would then invite volunteers from the audience to come up and place their heads on an obviously unprepared chopping block. Without any covering whatsoever, he would bring the ax smartly down on the neck of the spectator and the ax blade would pass through the neck cutting the block below in half ... with no damage to the neck! Hockmann says, "Axle, and his Magic Ax" gave up doing the act after several seasons because no one ever came up on stage to volunteer for his trick. Axle became a very fine barber and moved to Seville.

Human Sewing Machine

"The Great Antonio" was the first magician to perform the "Human Sewing Machine" act. The Great Antonio's current routine involved swallowing a pound of spaghetti, a dozen cloves of garlic and twenty-two Italian meat balls. His wife would grab one end of the spaghetti and pull it from his mouth displaying all twenty-two meat balls threaded on the spaghetti. For some reason, the act wasn't going over too well in the finest dinner show rooms.

In the 1850's, the new sewing machine was quite a sensation. So the great Antonio got the idea of swallowing a spool of thread, some needles, a bolt of linen and a Singer Sewing Machine ... complete with foot treadle. His wife would grab the end of the thread and pull out a complete wardrobe for milady. The act was an immediate success and the Great Antonio would have loved the acclaim ... if he had lived!

Rabbit in the Hat

"The Rabbit in the Hat" idea started in the year 1782. An unemployed magician, Ludwig VonPlatt, was staying at the famed Schtettgardt Hotel in Vienna, Austria. The hotel had very strict rules against cooking in the rooms. Since Ludwig and his wife couldn't afford to eat in the expensive hotel dining room, he fell into the habit of preparing Hossenpheffer over the open flame of his multiplying candle trick. For the principle ingredient, he would go into the hills, catch a rabbit, and sneak it into the fancy hotel under his top hat.

One day, Ludwig passed a beautiful lady in the lobby and gentlemanly doffed his hat ... right in front of a hotel manager! Thinking quickly, he pulled the rabbit out of the hat with a magical flourish and told the manager it was the newest trick in his act. The lady turned out to be the Queen of Bavaria. She was so impressed, she asked Ludwig to be her court magician and the rabbit-in-the-hat magician's trademark was born.

Asbestos

In 1827, a Frenchman named Chabert tested the heat resistance of asbestos by entering an oven wearing an asbestos suit with a steak in his hand. Twelve minutes later, he came out unharmed, holding his slightly overcooked steak. In today's enlightened world, we know that inhaling asbestos can be harmful to your health. Lucky for Chabert, he was able to hold his breath for twelve minutes while he was in that oven! (Harry Hockmann lost a small fortune in the sixties when he invested in asbestos cigarette paper.)

Mini-Illusion

Rupert VonBungle was the first magician to reverse the trend of making big stage illusions out of small tricks. He used the concepts of the big illusions to create micro magic effects which he performed in his close-up act. Magicians still talk of his "Sawing a Mouse in Half," "The Floating and Vanishing Flea" which was nicknamed by magicians "The Half Asrah." Rupert also did the "Substitution Cockroach Trunk" wherein the cockroach in a sequined dinner jacket changes places with a termite. One of his most charming micro magic tricks was his "Gnats in the Hat."

Cast Iron Balloon

Thaddeus S.C. Lowe was named official "Military Aeronaut" by President Abraham Lincoln in 1861. He organized the first balloon corps. A year later, impressed by the Confederate iron-clad warship, "Merrimac," Union Colonel Hezibal Montieth came up with his fifty-foot in diameter cast-iron hot air balloon. The balloon worked fabulously as long as it stayed on the ground. In fact, it helped win a major battle when it accidentally rolled down a hill and crushed a southern fort.

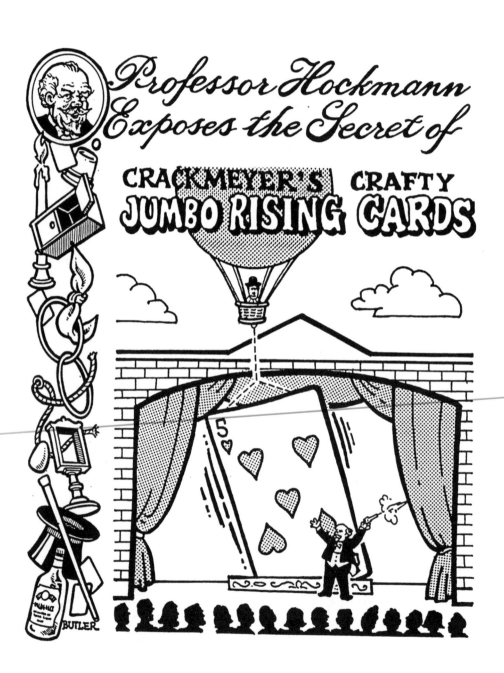

Professor Hockmann Exposes the Secret of

CRACKMEYER'S CRAFTY JUMBO RISING CARDS

BUTLER

THE JUMBO RISING CARDS

The old Professor used this legendary effect only once in the Appalachia Texas Opera House in 1910. This was the first use, on the American stage, of non-helium-filled playing cards. Crackmeyer's cards were as thin as cardboard, yet bigger than your average billboard. The obvious method of an invisible thread from the fly gallery was eliminated by having a committee from the audience station themselves in the fly loft during the performance.

The Secret:

I think you'll be absolutely fascinated by the simplicity of this amazing effect. The Professor did use regular magician's invisible thread ... BUT, it was not tied to a typical theater curtain batten! Instead, it went up through the rooftop air vent and was securely tied to the bottom of a hot air balloon hovering above the theater for advertising purposes! When the balloon pilot heard the sound of Hockmann's double-barreled sawed-off blank pistol, up went the balloon and, of course, up went the card! (They really should bring back some of these old magical principles.)

Human Vacuum

An inventor, Ives McGaffrey of Chicago, invented the vacuum cleaner in 1869 which led P.T. Barnum to comment "There's a sucker born every minute." Hockmann recalls an act from the early days of vaudeville, "The Great Sucko... the Human Vacuum Cleaner." This amazing performer was a skinny man who would invite members of the audience to litter the stage with sawdust, ashes, leaves, feathers, ink and glass. Then his assistant would hold him by the feet like a wheelbarrow and "The Great Sucko" would inhale the entire mess in less than two minutes. When he left the stage, he looked like a balloon. Hockmann watched from backstage as the stagehands carried him to the alley to empty him. Sucko passed away one night when someone added a truckload of corks to the litter of the stage. (They spent four days trying to bury "The Great Sucko" at sea.)

The Great Puzzelle

"The Great Puzzelle" made his American debut at the old Heggendorffer Opera House in Ohio. Puzzelle was a French magician who took tiny toy puzzles and made huge stage versions of them. It was hilarious to see two burly volunteers from the audience struggling with the old "Bent Nail Puzzle" made out of a one-inch diameter steel rod weighing two hundred pounds. One of Puzzelle's big routines involved four guys that stood at each corner of a twenty-four square piece of wood with holes at various intervals. By raising or lowering the square, they would roll a 200 pound bomb into progressive holes. One night, a live surplus bomb put an end to Puzzelle, the volunteers, the act ... and the old Heggendorffer Opera House in Ohio.

Lash & His Wonder Whip

In 1850, the United States Navy abolished the penalty of "flogging." After that, if you wanted to be flogged, you'd have to go flog yourself. Hockmann reminisces about many great whip marksmanship acts in vaudeville. The usual ones snapped cigarettes from their assistant's mouth or put out candles at forty paces. Harry's favorite flogger was "Lash and his Wonder Whip."

After doing the usual demonstrations, Lash invited a committee of men and women from the audience to join him on stage. The audience participation part of Lash's routine was the talk of show biz! The chosen audience members would line up on one side of the stage and Lash would take his place on the other side. Then Lash would proceed to pick off items of clothing from his volunteers. First a tie, then a button, then a belt, and so on. His big finish was getting one of his helpers down to his shorts.

This proved to be his big finish in more ways than one. One night he got carried away and his snapping bull whip tore away the volunteer's jockey shorts. The volunteer turned out to be the Police Commissioner of Boston who had come to check out the show. They say the other inmates enjoyed Lash's act at their Annual Boston Jail Christmas Party.

In his prime, Lash could pick up a fly off the end of a cigarette butt held in the mouth of his assistant "No Nose" Murphy at twenty paces. Lash could cut off the wick of a lit candle at thirty paces. Lash could outrun the town Marshal by forty paces. (Hockmann says there was no truth to the rumor that Lash used his whip on his wife for sadistic pleasure. Lash explained that his wife's back had those marks because of her odd habit of sleeping nude on a chain link fence.)

MAGNETO, THE GREAT

"The Great Magneto" was billed as "The Human Anchor." Magneto challenged a group of spectators to join him and lift him off the stage. Although he weighed a mere 200 pounds, no one could lift him no matter how hard he tried. Physical culture experts were astounded by this feat. Ten, twenty, thirty muscular men strained together and yet The Great Magneto's feet would never leave the floor.

The Secret:

The clever secret was to be found in his very special shoes. They contained a screw device that would auger into the stage floor at his command. The end of "The Human Anchor" happened when a group of college students challenged The Great Magneto on the iron platform of a train station in Cincinnati. Their combined lift shot him through the roof of the glass train shed. He became successful in later days as "The Tallest Man in the World."

Blindfold Act

On May 30, 1897, one of magic's greatest acts opened at the Lompoc Hippodrome in Lompoc, California. The act was Wing Ching Foo and Family. Wing Ching Foo would allow himself to be blindfolded by a committee of dentists from the audience. They would place two inverted tablespoons over his eyes, then squish some sour dough flapjack mix over his face, then dip his head in hot tar. It was virtually impossible for Wing Ching Foo to see. Ching Foo would place initialed bullets into a borrowed high-powered rifle and shoot out any tooth called for from the mouth of his son, Izzy. The secret was amazingly simple according to Hockmann. Ching Foo paid kids to pretend they were his son, Izzy.

Walking Across a River

In 1909, a young man by the name of Orville Wright surprised the nation by staying aloft for an amazing one hour, twelve minutes and forty seconds. His flying machine was now being called an "airplane." On the same day, in 1915, another pioneer, Homer C. Cecil, shocked the scientific world by walking across the Mississippi River. He invented special cork shoes to keep his feet above the water. Unfortunately, the cork shoes did keep his feet up ... which meant his head was down! (He left no heirs.)

Midget Menagerie

Phineas T. Barnum introduced Jumbo to the audiences of America. Jumbo, of course, was the largest elephant ever seen on the North American continent. Hockmann recalls this was also the date Lumbowski's "Midget Menagerie" opened in St. Louis in 1927. According to Hockmann, this was the greatest show featuring miniature animals. Billed as the "World's Smallest Arabian Steeds," Lumbowski's horses stood only 23 inches tall, without shoes. The tiny horses would do all the typical trained horse bits. (Some skeptics said his horses were actually Shetland Ponies.) His "World's Smallest Elephant" drew people from miles around. (Some skeptics said the elephant was a pig painted gray with a phony trunk.)

His midget giraffe was billed as "The World's Only Giraffe that Could Be Held in a Handbag." Of course, once the customers paid their money and got into the tent, they found the handbag was the size of a triple sleeping bag. Hockmann says Lumbowski was finally run out of town by some irate townspeople who discovered his "Man-eating Miniature Tiger" was a mean pussy cat named "Butch." The Midget Menagerie folded in 1928.

Daddy Kann

Andrew Carnegie established the Carnegie Institute in Washington, D.C. by donating a gift of ten million dollars. Hockmann was asked if he could remember any great philanthropic gifts to the art of magic. Hockmann came up with this little known magical fact: It seems the famed tin tycoon, Colonel "Daddy" Kann (the inventor of the "Tin Kann") was an avid magic enthusiast and amateur magician. He loved magic and he loved magicians. Above all, he loved his magic club, "The Conjuror's Chalet," a Victorian Chalet situated atop Pike's Peak. One day, The Colonel brought a group of his guests to the club to impress them with the art of magic. His guest of honor was the notable J. Rockefeller Getty-Morgan and his entourage of beautiful ladies. One member took a lady aside and exposed the secret of the invisible harpist. Another did the world's longest stack routine with a deck of cards using everything except the four aces. At dinner, the maitre d' made a pass at one of the ladies while two tourists in over-stuffed pantsuits asked J. Rockefeller for an autograph. Then "Daddy" got the check, which had been added incorrectly, and his name was misspelled. When The Colonel finally got his Rolls-Royce from the parking attendant, he noticed a new scratch in the twenty-five coats of lacquer and drove angrily away.

When Colonel "Daddy" Kann died, he was worth over a billion dollars. In his will, he left the magicians of "The Conjuror's Chalet" a silver dollar and told them where they could vanish it!

GREAT KIDDIE WONDER SHOW

Harry and Maude never had children. The only pitter-patter of tiny, little feet they had at the Rancho usually stopped after the monthly visit by the exterminator. Hockmann performed magic for adults but, in 1920, he did his first and last show for small children. "Professor Hockmann's Great Kiddie Wonder Show" didn't go over very well. Some of the kids didn't understand his big stage illusions. Most of the children in the audience were taken home in tears before the intermission. A few of the effects listed in a faded program found in the Magic Castle library provide a clue: "Swords Through Santa," "Sawing a Tooth Fairy in Half," and "Crushing a Teddy Bear."

DO YOU WANT YOUR KID'S BIRTHDAY TO BE
UNFORGETTABLE
???
Prof. Hockmann's
GREAT KIDDIE WONDER SHOW!
HA! HA! HA! HA! HA! HA! HA!
HILARIOUS FUN FOR EVERYONE!
HOCKMANN WILL PERFORM THIS COMEDY CLASSIC WITH YOUR KID'S TEDDY BEAR!
The KING of CUTE!
BIOPTIC!
BAFFLING!
BLOODLESS!
AFTER SEEING THIS SHOW, YOU WILL WONDER!

Mr. Explosive

September 3, 1927 was the day Mervyn Coy celebrated his combination debut and untimely passing. Mervyn worked under the stage name of "Mr. Explosive" and presented standard magic effects substituting the usual props with fireworks. For instance, he did the "Walsh Vanishing Skyrocket," "The Multiplying Cherry Bombs" and the "Cut and Restored Fuse." His biggie though, was swallowing a bunch of detonator caps, a couple sticks of dynamite and a roll of wire. Then he would pull the wire from his mouth and attach the loose end to a dynamite plunger. He would bring forth each and every stick of dynamite threaded to the wire. To add dramatic effect, Mervyn's wife, Sybil, would plunge the plunger in time to the music as each stick appeared causing that stick to explode. It was really a bang-up act and probably would have been a big success, if his wife hadn't jumped her music cue on that first fateful night.

Mathematical Tricks

Foo Yung Twang, a Chinese mathematical scholar, defeated Homer Von Shroppshire in a challenge between the ancient abacus and the modern calculator. This test took place in 1954 at Green Canyon, Montana. Twang was able to accomplish the square root of the sum of the multiple of twenty-seven in less time than it took Von Shroppshire to punch up the numbers on his calculator. Hockmann was kidding about the event at Rancho Hockmann and asked Maude to find the old board he used in a demonstration of mathematical magic. This is something you can try on your friends. It isn't magic, it is simply an arithmetic novelty. Ask your friend for the date of his (or her) birth. Whatever the number is, ask him (or her) to divide it by the number of children in his (or her) family. This sum is then multiplied by the total amount of loose change in his (or her) pocket at the time of the test. At this point, and this is very important, ask someone in the audience how many eggs make a dozen. Someone in the audience will invariably shout out "twelve." This number must be subtracted to obtain the total. The number, of course, will be 1776, which is not only astounding, but downright patriotic.

Million Dollar Marvo

"Marvo, the Million Dollar Magic Man" did a theme act with bills and coins. He would cause dimes to turn to quarters, quarters to halves, halves to silver dollars, silver to gold. His borrowed thousand dollar bill in the cigarette was an absolute smash (until one night his wife smoked the wrong cigarette backstage.) Marvo's big finish was exploding a large weather balloon filled with twenty dollar bills which would fall from the ceiling of the theater. There was always a standing ovation at this point of his act which never failed to impress managers. Marvo stopped doing the act on Halloween night, 1929, due to the unfortunate demise of his financial backer two days earlier when the stock market crashed.

Professor Hockmann Exposes the Secret of

The Vanishing Dime
EXTRAVAGANZA

VANISHING DIME EXTRAVAGANZA

On August 25, 1879 Gilbert and Sullivan's "Pinafore" was performed in its most spectacular version. It was done on a real ship floating in a man-made lake in the middle of New York's Madison Square Garden. Hockmann always believed in elaborate staging. Even the smallest tricks were given full production in "The Great Hockmann Show." His "Vanishing Dime Trick" alone required two truckloads of special scenery, lighting, fountains, and a dime.

Magic Opera

The first magic opera ever performed in the United States was written by Puccini "Curley" Von Verde, an American from the garlic fields of Detroit. The opera, called "Asrah," was about a beautiful queen who floated over her kingdom under a sheet. As the story unfolded in this magnificent opera, Asrah is surrounded by her enemies in the Temple of Benaresin in the second act. Her would-be captors grabbed her sheet as she was floating and yanked it away. She vanished in thin air! Asrah, played by a diva weighing three hundred pounds, plus, suddenly reappeared hanging by her toes in the dome of the theater, high above the audience. Her final aria was "Si mi Domo Creppeccio" which, literally translated means, "Get me down from here!" The opera opened and had its final performance on the same night after the diva fell on the owner of the Grumple Opera House, the Mayor of the town, the Chief of Police, and the Temple of Benarsein.

Deflyto, The Great

"Deflyto, The Great" was a daring young man who built very clever metal wings that attached to his arm. He claimed he could soar from the top of the Empire State Building in New York City to Staten Island in less time than it would take the building's elevator to get from the top floor to the street level.

The high school brass band was waiting to welcome him at the Staten Island Ferryboat landing, but "Deflyto, The Great" never got any further than 34th Street. (However, he did beat the elevator to street level!) The combination debut and farewell performance of "Deflyto, The Great" happened on April 14, 1934.

Professor Harry Hockmann

AKA

HOCKMANN, THE GREAT

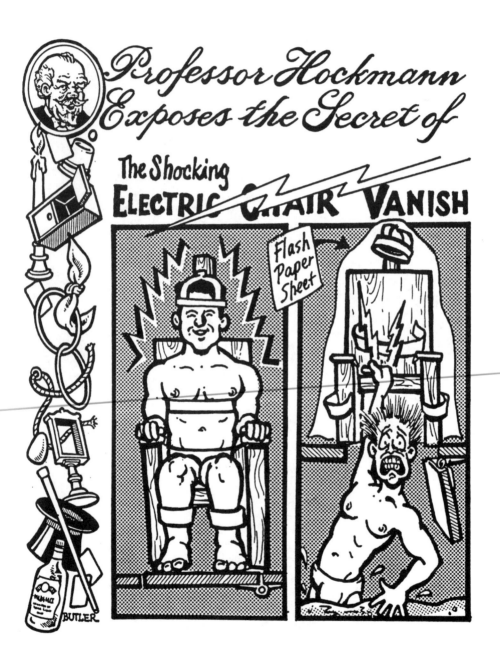

SHOCKING ELECTRIC CHAIR VANISH

In 1890, William Kemmer became famous as the first person to be executed in the "Electric Chair." The event inspired a magician, "The Great Ampere" to create a sensational new illusion, "Vanish Du Seat l'Hotte." A metal electric chair was attached to a 400,000 volt generator on stage, operated by a huge knife switch. The Great Ampere allowed himself to be shackled to the chair wearing only a metallic bikini. He was then covered with a sheet (actually a huge piece of magician's flash paper). As the band played, "There'll be a Hot Time in the Old Town Tonight," an assistant threw the switch. In a shower of sparks and fire, The Great Ampere was gone.

The Secret:

The secret, according to Hockmann, was very simple. A well-known fact is that electricity is harmless unless it is grounded. The metal chair was totally insulated from any sort of ground connection. The magician used his binding chains to lower himself through a trap door into the basement below for the big vanish. (His career came to a rather abrupt halt when a water pipe burst, flooding the basement of the theater before his act.)

HOCKMANN ON INVENTIONS

In his retirement from the stage, Harry Hockmann has used his large illusion manufacturing workshop at Rancho Hockmann to invent things. He invented glasses with little rearview mirrors so he could see whether he was coming or going. Most of his inventions haven't been too successful but, as Harry says, "All you need is one safety pin!" A few of his failures include the "Solid Buttonhole," "The Double Pointed Thumb Tack," and "The Solid Drinking Straw."

Few people realize Hockmann has many patents to his name. For instance, he invented concrete bicycle tires for use on rubber bike paths. He was the first one to control the speed of a horse with his electric horse saddle. He introduced the steel windshield to the auto industry. He holds the patent on the reversible sump pump and improved on Tom Edison's electric incandescent light bulb by filling it with water to keep the filament cool.

All these items can be seen on display at the Hockmann Hall of Science located at Rancho Hockmann behind the tool shed.

Hockmann recently invented the "Electronic Cheating Bathroom Scale." It looks like any other scale and registers the perfect weight for anyone who steps on it. BUT, the buyer gets a tiny electronic device which can be discretely hidden even while nude and can be set to alter the reading of the scale by as much as twenty pounds! Thus, you can go on a diet and show the family that you are losing several pounds every day. As backup, Hockmann also plans to market phony tape measures and counterfeit labels to sew in your waistband. Potential investors should contact Harry at Rancho Hockmann as soon as possible. Don't miss out on this one!

Hockmann is known in magic circles as the inventor of many stage illusions. He claims credit for the world's first "Hot Air Floating Lady," the "Horizontal Hindu Rope Trick," and the "Flush Appearance," otherwise known as "The Girl in the Tidy Bowl."

Harry discovered a new plastic material that is absolutely invisible. Think of the magical use for the stuff! His only problem is, he can't remember where he got it and he laid it down somewhere where he can't find it.

In 1811, Tom Edison filed papers for his very first invention. It was an electrical vote recorder which was designed to tabulate floor votes in Congress. Congress rejected it because it saved too much time. Hockmann invented the world's first muck-rake back in the 30's. He thought it would be a big hit with muckraking politicians. The invention might have been a success if there had been more muck on the market. As it was, no one was making muck so there was little muck to rake except, of course, at election time. Hockmann still has some of his original muckrakes in the shop at Rancho Hockmann.

Hockmann's latest invention is a "Tamper-Proof Lunch Box" which can't be opened. When the obvious problem with this idea was mentioned, Harry quickly said it would be great for people who are always on diets.

Harry has always wondered which came first, the button or the button hole. He had a friend who was the epitome of the frustrated inventor. It seems he invented half of the zipper.

Few people realize that the saxophone was invented by a Belgian named Adolph Sax about 1840. The Sousaphone was, of course, invented by the great military band leader, John Philip Sousa. Alexander Graham Bell wanted to call his new invention the "Bellyphone." Hockmann invented a musical instrument called the "Hockophone" in 1938. It was the amplified sound of a fingernail scraping a blackboard in variable pitches. It wasn't successful as a musical instrument so Harry sold it to the military for the potential use during World War II as a torture device.

Professor Hockmann Exposes the Secret of
The Aerially Astounding
VANISHING FLYING MACHINE

VANISHING FLYING MACHINE ILLUSION

On March 30, 1858, Hyman L. Lippman patented the first pencil equipped with an eraser. Hymie would have been better known today if someone hadn't erased his name from the history books. It is also the anniversary of the date in 1924 when Professor Hockmann startled the magic world with his "Vanishing Flying Machine Illusion." Harry said he had to invent this illusion because of a typographical error. It seems one of the features of his show of '24 was the "Vanishing Sewing Machine Illusion" but the poster artist made a slight mistake. 50,000 full color lithographs were made plugging the "Flying Machine." Hockmann made a deal with Wilbur and Orville Bratenhoffer for a used World War I biplane and vanished it using a principle that has been grossly overlooked by modern magicians.

The Secret:

Under the cover of a very large foulard, Hockmann's assistants stood the plane on its nose and flipped some scenic pieces in front of the plane. This made the plane appear like an ornamental water fountain, lost in Hockmann's very busy potted palm-filled set. The audience was so astonished at the disappearance of the plane that they failed to notice the addition of the fountain.

Invention of the Wheel

The wheel, as we know it today, was invented by Wilbur and Orville Grunt. They were Stone Age brothers who discovered the wheel by accident as they tried to even off the corners of a large slab of granite. The rock started to roll down a slope and the brothers noted it moved faster and smoother than their experiments with cubes and square rocks. The neighbors in the caves were impressed that their disk rock created less noise pollution than the square "wheel."

It took another inventor, Horatio Arrgh, to really make the wheel practical. Horatio came up with the idea of putting a hole in the middle of the wheel and letting the stone revolve around a wooden shaft. Horatio called this shaft an "Arrgh." Maude Hockmann says the old Professor knows a lot about the Stone Age since he's been stoned most of his old age.

Botania, The Great

The world's greatest flower production act was done around the turn of the century by a magician named "The Great Botania." The act opened with Botania driving out on stage in a new "Horseless Carriage." He was immaculately dressed in the latest style white duster, cap and goggles. He would present bare-handed productions of hundreds of fresh roses, rose bushes with thorns, and vines of climbing roses. As he would produce the flowers, he would place them artistically on his automobile. At the finale of his act, The Great Botania would jump back into the car, lower his goggles, and drive off stage. A traveling chewing gum salesman caught his act one day and sped back to Pasadena, California where he sold the City Fathers on the idea of using rose-covered "floats" for their New Year's Day parade. The irony of this is, two years later, Botania's entire act was eaten by a horde of Japanese beetles.

Full Light Vanish Illusion

Back in 1906, Professor Hockmann delighted his audience at the old Cleveland Athenaeum and Music Hall with his often imitated but seldom repeated "Vanish of the Magician in Full Light Illusion." This great effect marked the first use of a trap by a magician. The trap, it seems, was left in the stage by a split week road company of "Madame Butterfly." In their haste to leave town, they took all the box office cash but left their props and Madame Butterfly behind. The stage manager covered the open hole in the stage with a large piece of paper. On the night of March 11, 1906, "Hockmann, The Great" made his usual entrance down a set of steps, flanked on each side by his company of the local beauty contest runner-ups and his wife, Maude. Hockmann marched down the stairs producing red, white and blue paper flowers from a large foulard to the orchestral strains of "Pomp and Circumstance." It was flawless until he reached the stage level. The resulting "vanish" was unexpected by the audience, the cast, and Hockmann. The trap was immediately established as a standard magician's gimmick. Hockmann removed the hole in the Cleveland Athenaeum stage and took it with him for the remainder of his tour, which resumed after his broken legs mended.

Professor Hockmann Exposes the Secret of

The Fakir's Favorite
HINDU ROPE TRICK

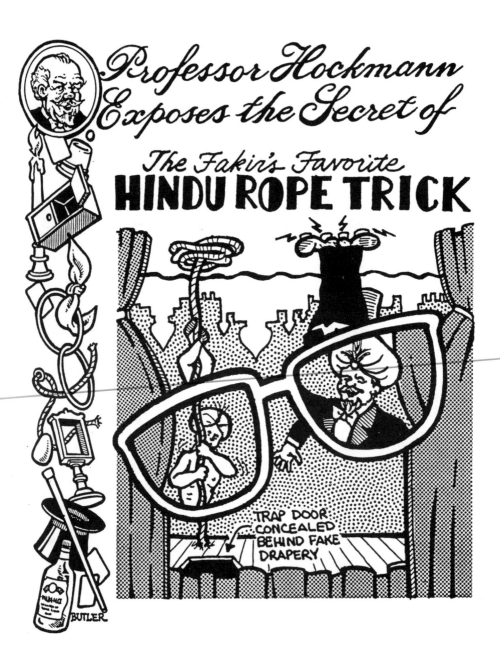

TRAP DOOR
CONCEALED
BEHIND FAKE
DRAPERY

BUTLER

THE FAKIR'S FAVORITE HINDU ROPE TRICK

"The Hindu Rope Trick" was performed by "Hockmann, The Great" in 1923. Everyone knows the legendary effect, but Hockmann's method was quite revolutionary.

The Secret:

Hockmann had a scenic ceiling painted to look like the stage floor and the floor was painted to look like a ceiling. The backdrop was hung upside down. The curtains opened on Hockmann, in Indian costume, as he stood on the stage with a coil of rope and a native kid. In reality, Hockmann and the kid were fastened to the ceiling with magnetic shoes and were hanging upside down. The rest is obvious. Hockmann would release the rope, which would fall down and the kid would then slide down the rope upside-down and wave at the bottom. At a flash of smoke, the kid dropped into a trap on the stage and "vanished." It was another simple "modus operandi" overlooked by many of our younger illusionists. By the way, each person in the audience had to wear special prism eyeglasses which made the upside-down set look right-side up.

Titanic Illusion

After striking an iceberg on April 12, 1912, the unsinkable British luxury liner Titanic sank off Cape Race, Newfoundland. According to Hockmann, he was the first one to introduce a major stage spectacle to Las Vegas audiences at one of the town's first big hotel: The Las Vegas Baths and Casino. Through magical illusion, the audience really believed they saw the great ship, Titanic, sink before their very eyes. (Note: *As Hockmann, The Great's biographer, your writer has found that "Hock," as he is called by his close friends, tends to elaborate on the truth from time to time. In this case, when questioned about this rather hard-to-believe story, Harry thumbed through an old scrapbook and produced a review headed: "Vegas Hockmann Show Recalls the Sinking of the Titanic." And other, "Hockmann Magic Show - a Real Disaster." I am sorry we doubted the great magician.*)

Lightning Trio

Ben Franklin discovered electricity when his wife told him to "go fly a kite." Without electricity, Thomas Edison's light bulb was just another idea and magicians would have had to think up another title for the "electric deck." Of course, electricity had been around for a long time, but nobody knew what it was good for until Ben Franklin figured it out. Hockmann remembers an old vaudeville act called "The Lightning Trio." The gimmick was three guys had high voltage wired to their metal tap shoes and danced on a charged copper plate stage. One day, the guy in the middle lost his balance and grabbed the other two, electrocuting them instantly. "Shorty" continued as a single until his fuse failed on a rainy night in Pittsburgh.

Mountain From a Molehill Trick

Back in 1923, Professor Hockmann first presented his, now famous, "Mountain Out of a Molehill" trick. The curtains opened on a rural scene with a common ordinary unprepared molehill down stage center. A fanfare from the band and Hockmann's two assistants would guide Hockmann on stage.

(This was a common practice in later years, because of Hockmann's advanced age. In 1923, it was more than likely due to the inconsistencies of rot gut bootleg hooch!)

The Professor would then show both hands empty, reach magically into the thin air, and produce a cascade of genuine dirt. The dirt would flow down on top of the molehill and, in time, a large mountain would form in front of the eyes of the bewildered spectators. (Note: *As truly great an illusion as this was, Hockmann later cut it out of his show. The complete effect took under two days to perform and Hockmann often sensed he was losing his audience.*)

Great Water Balloon

Hockmann likes to talk about the team of well-known inventors, John Reed, Wilbur and Orville Wright, and Alphonse Rithmetic, forming a new combo called, "Reed, Wright and A. Rithmetic."

Their goal was to invent a safe dirigible. (The Hindenberg had exploded and burned just a couple of months before at Lakehurst, New Jersey.) Their solution was to fill the dirigible with the world's most common fire quencher. It proved to be highly unsuccessful. When the huge water-filled balloon was launched off the top floor of one of New York's tallest skyscrapers, many people said it reminded them of the demise of King Kong, atop the Empire State Building.

Professor Hockmann Exposes the Secret of

THE REPULSIVE REPTILIAN
Cut & Restored Rattlesnake

"DUPLI-SNAKE" SLITHERS FROM SLEEVE INTO TUBE

"LATE SNAKE" DROPS INTO LAP

THE CUT & RESTORED RATTLESNAKE

Here's another Hockmann original effect you can do. Display a live rattlesnake to your audience. (Take care not to let the rubber bands slip off its mouth since the bite of a "rattler" can be rather uncomfortable.) Show a common, ordinary sheet of paper ... the Playboy fold-out is the right size for your average snake, and it also provides an entertainment plus for the gentlemen in the audience. Wrap the paper around the snake and then dramatically cut the paper tube in half using common, ordinary hedge clippers. Scotch tape the two halves of the paper back together again, unroll it, and the snake slithers out onto the table unharmed.

The Secret:

This trick is very simple and, of course, involves the use of an exact duplicate rattlesnake. Under the misdirection of taping the two halves of the tube together, the paper is held in a vertical position and the original snake, which we shall refer to as "The Late Snake" drops unnoticed into the magician's lap. At this point, the duplicate snake slithers out of your sleeve and crawls into the tube. The rest of the presentation is obvious. (Note: *A slight amount of patience is required in training your rattlesnake to slither out of your sleeve into the tube without making noise.* Note II: *Hockmann suggests not performing his close-up effect if you are already doing a standard "Rat Act."*)

Igloo Revue of '22

Hockmann's "Igloo Revue of 1922" introduced a brand new version of the "Broom Suspension Illusion" in a scene wherein the girls were dressed as dancing polar bears. They broke icicles off the scenery and did a military drill team number with them. One of the girls, costumed as an Eskimo, was then propped up with two five-foot icicles under her arms. One icicle was removed, ala the broom trick, and the girl was suspended in mid-air. The nice thing about this unique effect was that the girl was laughing most of the time, since she was a bit ticklish. Another nice bit was the automatic lowering of the girl to the stage floor as the ice melted.

Hot Air Straight Jacket Escape

In 1923, Harry Houdini thrilled a huge New York City audience by hanging upside-down forty feet in the air and escaping from a regulation straight jacket. The event made front pages throughout the world.

Professor Hockmann claims he invented the straight jacket escape months before Houdini attempted it. According to Hockmann, he got the idea while recuperating from an attack of delirium tremens at the Happy Acres Sanitarium. One day, he got an inspiration to escape from his straight jacket hanging upside-down from a hot air balloon. Everything seemed fine until they lit the bonfire to make the hot air for the balloon ascension. By the time Hockmann got out of the burn ward at the hospital, Houdini had stolen his idea.

Kidd Hanging

In 1699, the famous pirate Captain Kidd was arrested in Boston and deported to England. It saved Captain Kidd from having to purchase a full fare ticket on a luxury schooner. Hockmann's favorite pirate was "Long John Silver" who got his nickname because he was always cold and wore three layers of red flannel underwear under his pirate suit.

Harry also says the old vaudevillian expression "give 'em the hook" started in the days of the pirates. If one of the ship's entertainers was lousy, "getting the hook" was a very painful experience. It was, however, better than "being on the boards" which, in pirate talk, meant walking the plank.

Captain William Kidd was hanged May 23rd, 1785. Hockmann commemorated the event in "The Great Hockmann Show" of 1925 with "The Hanging of Kidd Illusion Spectacle." As usual, Harry got his facts a little screwed up and mixed up Billy, the Kid and Captain Kidd, and the Stage Manager's kid. Somehow, the 1925 audiences weren't quite ready for hanging a ten year old kid in cowboy chaps from the yardarm of a Spanish galleon.

Pictures-To-Life Illusion

Hockmann points out the early movies were considered magic. He recalls that a French magician, Monsieur Emile DePathe, opened a theater devoted exclusively to moving pictures in Paris. The French police closed down the place after only two weeks and jailed both DePathe, the live dancers and his partner, an extremely talented lightning tattoo artist. Hockmann also talked about the first use of "Pictures-to-Life Illusion" wherein the picture on the screen actually turns into a living person. Hockmann modestly says he invented this great effect quite accidentally when his wife, Maude, served him a dish of vanilla pudding for dessert. Harry noticed that, after eating a spoonful of pudding, the rest of the pudding would appear to reseal itself. (Try this yourself at home, it's really amazing!) The rest of the story is history. Hockmann had a full-size motion picture screen fabricated out of vanilla pudding.

Tom Edison

The electric incandescent bulb was patented by Thomas A. Edison in 1880. Many magicians think the light bulb was invented by magician Marvyn Roy, "Mr. Electric." Edison, later, crossed the light bulb with his earlier invention, the phonograph, and got something that keeps talking when lit. Maude says that sounds like Harry Hockmann! Harry claims he was a great friend of Tom Edison's and can prove it by showing you a gift from Tom, which Harry says, Edison gave him on his deathbed in 1931. It is a personally initialed incandescent light bulb. The initials are there, plain to see. (In certain light the "T" looks more like a "G." But the initialed incandescent light bulb remains another priceless memento from the Hockmann archives.)

Floating Cannonball

The premiere performance, in 1924, was Professor Hockmann's famous magical attempt, "The Floating Cannonball." In his presentation, a group of "plants" from the audience would attest to the fact that the cannonball in the act was genuine and weighed almost 200 pounds.

Then, with a wave of Hockmann's magical hands, the ball would rise in the air and float in space. Everything went fine that first night ... until the professor tried to prove the absence of any wires by passing a band saw blade over the cannonball. A sharp metallic twang was heard and the ball dropped through the floor, created a catapult effect on a loose board which sent Hockmann up into the fly gallery. Hockmann's original cannonball is still the object of curious conversation in the sub-basement of the old Bijou Opera House in Quacksbury, Missouri.

Sawing ala Hockmann

Professor Hockmann claims he invented the famed "Sawing a Woman in Half Illusion." A British magician, P.T. Selbit, later got credit for the invention, but Harry Hockmann's version was a full year ahead of Selbit. The illusion looked the same and the effect was the same. Even the giant logger's saw was purchased from the same manufacturer! The only difference between the Selbit Sawing and the Hockmann Sawing was that the "Selbit Sawing" worked! Hockmann gave up sawing ladies in half after some rather unfavorable publicity.

Crystal Set

Hockmann remembers buying his first crystal set. It came complete with a book on fortune telling and a deck of tarot cards. Harry once predicted the final scores of a World Series game and had the prediction sealed in an iron strong box which was welded shut and tossed off the Brooklyn Bridge. Hockmann says his prediction was absolutely correct and his fans would have been very impressed if they had only been able to find the box.

THE GUILLOTINE ILLUSION

Professor Hockmann first performed the French Guillotine Illusion in America in the year 1941. Hockmann also claims to be the first one to do a "midnight spook show" with his "Harry Hockmann's Horror House Revue of 1924" where the guillotine was introduced. His guillotine was two hundred, forty-two feet tall with a blade weighing over two hundred pounds. The first time Hockmann performed the effect, the blade slid down the guide posts, through the girl's neck, without any harm ... but made a nasty hole in the stage floor. Hockmann solved this problem with one hundred, seventy-five pounds of counterweights. The next time he presented the illusion, the blade whisked through the girl's neck without harm ... but the blade broke off at the bottom and the counterweights went up — taking the one hundred ten pound girl with them. Luckily, the crashing of her head against the top of the guillotine stocks broke the counterweights off, so the girl dropped to safety twenty-four feet below. (She was unhurt ... until the one hundred, seventy-five pounds of counterweights fell on her.)

Hockmann's Steam Bird

In 1932, Professor Hockmann startled the magic fraternity with his announcement of his invention of a steam driven mechanical bird. The Professor had already perfected the electric rabbit, but his steam bird was considered somewhat of a personal triumph.

One day, a real live white dove broke into Hockmann's dressing room with an eye towards an amorous adventure with the steam bird. In the course of that evening, the mechanical bird blew its boiler and was never seen on the American stage again. (Note: *Just before his retirement, the Professor was reported to have invented an atomic bird. Unfortunately, the atomic bird proved too expensive for the average dove act and, therefore, has never replaced your standard wind-up bird. Drop by Rancho Hockmann any time and ask the old Professor to show you his bird.*)

Bird Box Trick

One night Harry's head assistant, Moe Klopstein, tripped over the floating cannonball cable and squashed the Professor's bird. Since Moe was afraid the Professor would fire him for his carelessness, he captured an untrained city pigeon and substituted it for the Professor's specially trained magic dove. Hockmann, The Great showed his black-art bird box empty, as usual, that fateful night and pressed the button which opened the trap door, releasing the bird. The pigeon, not being in show biz, developed a severe case of stage fright upon seeing the live audience and the glare of the limelight.

Accidents will happen. Quick thinking, Hockmann ad-libbed that the folks had just witnessed his latest miracle, "The Color Changing Bird Box" and the audience never knew the difference. Hockmann kept the pigeon in the act ... on a very strict diet, and actually gave Moe Klopstein a raise.

Floating & Vanishing Cement Truck

Hockmann, The Great's "Floating and Vanishing Cement Truck Illusion" was performed for the first and last time on stage of the old Ogelthorpe Opera House, in Snaketongue, Arizona on September 29, 1936. Originally, Hockmann designed the illusion as a simple cement truck levitation, the vanish was purely accidental. He used a borrowed cement mixer and asked men from the local cement company to attest to the fact that it was filled with a full load of churning cement. Using the device of hundreds of invisible piano wires, Hockmann caused the cement truck to rise and seemingly float in midair.

Unfortunately, the gridiron of the old Ogelthorpe was not engineered to carry such a heavy load and gave way during Hockmann's act. The cement truck crashed through the floor and came to rest in the musician's rehearsal hall directly below the stage, narrowly missing Mrs. Hockmann and a piccolo player from Cincinnati whom Maude had dated in high school. The audience was absolutely baffled by the instant "vanish" of the truck and gave Harry a standing ovation as they ran from the theater.

Invisible Actor

Harry, it seems, invested money in a film called "The Invisible Exhibitionist." The star of the picture is never seen because he is invisible. Hockmann claims the producer hired one of the biggest names in the business to play the part. The opening scene finds a trench coat floating down the street which opens itself at a bus stop.

Harry also tells of a provocative scene where the trench coat is seen crumpled on the floor next to a draped table in the town's fanciest restaurant. You never see the Invisible Exhibitionist but you know he's there by the reaction of the couple dining at the table. The "Hot Tub Scene" is a triumph in special effects.

Floating Bathtub

Hockmann, The Great's "Floating Bathtub Illusion" uses an ordinary old-fashioned cast-iron claw-ball bathtub, which was brought on stage and shown empty. Hockmann's core of assistants marched on with buckets of warm water and filled the tub. His lovely head assistant, Fifi LaTour, danced on, looking not unlike an American flag ... probably one of the first uses of body painting in theater history. Fifi jumped in the tub and worked up a bunch of bubbles as Hockmann made some mysterious moves. As the audience stood in utter amazement, the entire bathtub started to rise in the air ... up ... and up until the tub and the lady were easily ten feet in the air.

With a flourish, Hockmann covered the tub with a huge bath towel, and then whipped it away. Both the tub and the lady were gone! (Note: *Hockmann, The Great dropped the illusion from future shows because most theaters of the day didn't have warm water and Fifi refused to sit in an icy tub. Also, the body paint of the day was watercolor which washed off the minute Fifi stepped in the soapy water, causing problems with the local sheriff. Additionally, it was very inconvenient working on a flooded stage after the tub had vanished ... Hockmann never quite worked out how to vanish the water.*)

Moby Dick Trick

Hockmann almost went broke in 1936 trying to develop a "Vanishing Whale Illusion." Stage magicians had done a vanishing automobile, a vanishing horse, and Houdini had vanished an elephant. But a whale? That could bring the Hockmann show back to prominence.

Hockmann felt the illusion would have worked if he could have only found the right theater in which to play. What Hockmann needed was a theater with a 30' by 30' by 80' glass water tank with a trap in the bottom. He even had a great name for the vanishing whale illusion worked out: "Moby Trick."

Girl, Slingshot and Concrete Wall Illusion

Hockmann creates magical illusions for professionals at his shop at Rancho Hockmann. Despite Harry's advancing years, he has one of the most fertile magical brains in the business. His newest illusion was tested recently. It is called "The Girl, The Slingshot and the Concrete Wall Illusion."

The effect is simple: a group of contractors from the audience build a concrete block wall on stage. The magician, then, displays a huge slingshot which is pulled into firing position by a small elephant. A girl is placed in the sling and shot through the concrete into a butterfly net on the other side of the wall. At testing Harry's wife, Maude, played the part of the girl. At this writing, she is recuperating nicely at the Happy Valley Sanitarium near the estate and should be out of her casts by next year.

Big Balloon Animals

Professor Hockmann made magical history by doing "Balloon Animal Illusions." Instead of little poodle dogs and swans, Hockmann made elephants and dinosaurs. Harry explained that the entire act came about because he stumbled upon a tremendous buy in surplus barrage balloons after World War II.

Hockmann got a sweet deal on surplus "K-Rations" which Maude says they will serve to guests on special occasions. Hockmann bought a surplus Army Tank which he erroneously believed to be amphibious. It can be seen rusting away at the bottom of Lake Hockmann at the Rancho.

Telephone Book Tear

Professor Hockmann amazed a number of his friends at a party when, at his advanced age, he actually ripped a telephone book in half! Of course, the book was the Scott's Bluff, Utah phone directory. Population: 28. Then he bet he could do the same thing with the L.A. Directory. He did rip the entire 1,268 page Pacific Bell white pages in half ... one page at a time!

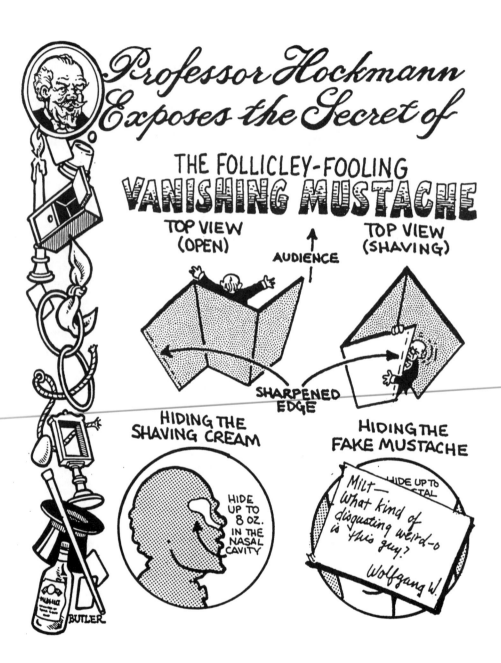

THE VANISHING MUSTACHE TRICK

In 1939, Harry Hockmann startled Broadway with his vanishing and reappearing mustache trick. The effect was marvelous in its simplicity. While a committee from the audience inspected a solid steel three-fold screen, Hockmann would flash on stage stark naked, ala Harry Houdini, and allow himself to be searched for a hidden razor or shaving mug. Then, a group of well-known barbers would tug and pull on Harry's flowing handlebar mustache to make certain it was not phony. Hockmann jumped behind the screen ... a drum roll ... and seconds later the screen would drop to the floor AND Hockmann would appear with his upper lip sans hirsute adornment. As the audience would gasp and cheer, he would then whirl around and the mustache would reappear instantly. It was a great effect and the talk of New York.

The Secret:

Hockmann has given us permission to include the secret in these pages. Prior to coming on stage, Hockmann would secret a small amount of shaving cream up his nose. This went unnoticed in the search because in those days, a lot of people sounded like Rudy Vallee. The steel screen was sharpened on the inner edge. By running his lip up and down, he could easily shave off his real mustache very quickly. The reappearance involved hiding an exact duplicate phony mustache on his naked body which, again, was simple but not fit for publication.

Electric Eel Effect

"Hockmann, The Great" introduced a brand new magical effect called "The Eel Effect." (Actually, it was a clever switch on the cut and restored rope.) Hockmann started by introducing a live electric eel in an aquarium. He would, then, prove the eel's electricity level by letting it light up an incandescent lamp, run a motor and power a toaster. Then, using insulated gloves, the Professor would yank the eel from the aquarium and cut it into bits with a large sushi knife. He reassembled the pieces of eel, made a magic pass, and voila! The eel was alive and squiggling in the form of a neon letter "H."

Ice Tricks

Ice was discovered in Alaska. Hockmann had wanted to do a complete magic act using ice as a theme. (Think of all the standard tricks that could be switched to ice!) The old egg bag could be done with a cube of ice and the resulting "ice bag" would not only be mystifying but quite handy in case of a hangover. How about a "Walsh Vanishing Icicle"? The "Sucker Sliding Ice Box"? Or the "Torn and Restored Glacier"? All these are standard effects that could be worked with ice. Harry suggests closing the act with a diminishing twenty-five pound cake of ice, wherein the block of ice would visibly get smaller before the eyes of the astonished audience. Hockmann tested this illusion at the Rancho workshop and found a really hot spotlight reduces the time of the trick down to eighteen minutes.

Big Bertha Illusion

It was from the Civil War that the Professor got one of his greatest ideas for a stage illusion. "The Shooting a Girl from a Cannon Illusion." First, Hockmann would introduce "Big Bertha," played by Maude Hockmann. He would, then, stuff Maude in a cannon with the help of two very strong assistants.

As the military band played one of George M. Cohan's patriotic ditties, Hockmann took careful aim at a trunk suspended from the dome of the pawn shop across the street. The cannon was fired, the trunk was immediately brought down and on stage, opened ... and there was Maude crammed inside the trunk!

Hockmann has pieces of the original cannon in his warehouse today. It seems the cannon blew up one night after the Annual Prestidigitator's Picnic in Peoria, which also happened to be the occasion of Maude's winning the pie-eating contest.

Professor Hockmann Exposes the Secret of

THE TIME CONSUMPTIVE
NEST OF BOXES

NEST OF BOXES

Harry Hockmann says he invented the now famous magical effect, "The Nest of Boxes" in 1917. (Hockstorians argue this claim saying the trick goes back hundreds of years before 1917 and was probably Chinese in origin.) Hockmann says his version was much bigger and grander than any of the standard methods and he describes it like this: Twelve beautiful chorus girls would dance into the audience and borrow twelve pocket watches from the spectators. These borrowed watches were placed in a small velvet sack which was then "accidentally dropped" as the girls danced back on stage. At this point, a gigantic steam roller chugged across the stage squashing the watches in the sack to the delight of the other members of the audience. "Hockmann, The Great" would then dash over, pick up the sack, and listen to the tinkle of the broken parts, and then dramatically turn the sack inside out. The watches have vanished! A circus whistle pierced the air and a company of clowns and acrobats wheeled out a huge toy building block marked with the letter "A." This block was opened and another block "B" was found inside. The block "B" was opened to discover block "C" and this procedure was followed through twenty-five blocks until they got to block "Y" only to find block "Z." To the amazement of the audience, inside that block was a watermelon which was cut open to find a bottle of champagne which, in turn, was broken open to reveal a sealed cigar box. Finally each cigar was broken open to find the borrowed watch!

Time of act: 48 minutes.

HOCKMANN ON PUBLICITY

One of the reasons Hockmann, The Great Show did so well was Hockmann's great knack for getting free publicity. Hockmann gives most of the credit for this publicity to his advance man, Norman C. Tubthumper. Harry says the only thing Norman couldn't get in advance was his salary. Tubthumper would take advantage of every opportunity to get publicity. One day in Butte, Montana, Hockmann heard that a man had been found frozen in a cake of ice. Scientists agreed that he might come back to life when he was thawed out. Norman immediately put out the word that the man in the ice was Hockmann's Uncle Louie, who had been lost with the second company of the Hockmann show in Alaska.

Naturally, the papers jumped on this and Hockmann agreed to be there for the defrosting ceremonies. Then, Norman convinced the papers that they should insist the defrosting be delayed until after Hockmann's local run so "no one could say this was a cheap publicity stunt." The publicity and the anticipation continued and the show was sold out for the entire run. Hockmann and Norman C. Tubthumper feigned surprise when the man in the cake of ice turned out to be an inebriated worker in the local ice plant.

Torpedo Escape

It was in 1864 that the Civil War Commander David Farragut spoke his famous words, "Damn the torpedoes ... full speed ahead!" Actually, it's rumored that the statement was altered slightly for history's sake. The real historic words were, "Damn! ... They've got torpedoes! ... Full speed ahead! ... Let's get the hell out of here!!!" One of Hockmann's best publicity stunts was his "Blindfold Torpedo Drive." Hockmann would let a committee of press representatives chain him to a live torpedo, blindfold him with a steel swim mask, fire the torpedo at a target a mile away. Then, Hockmann would make his escape before the torpedo made contact with the target. Hockmann gave up doing this stunt shortly after a close encounter with a lovesick shark who mistook the speeding torpedo and its rider for a missing girlfriend.

Lindbergh

Charles A. Lindbergh made the first solo flight across the Atlantic in 1927. "Lucky Lindy" climbed into the monoplane and took off for Paris. Thirty-three and a half hours later, he landed and became a National hero. Isn't it amazing that now, with the Concorde, you can make the same flight in about three hours. Of course, with airport parking, check-ins and customs, it still takes about thirty-three hours!

The day Lindy landed, Professor Hockmann climaxed, what should have been, the world's greatest publicity stunt. He escaped from a straight jacket while hanging upside-down from the top of the Eiffel Tower. Since most Parisians were more interested in "Lucky Lindy" than "Hanging Hocky," the stunt drew a smaller crowd than the Annual Escargot Races. Hockmann was so angry, he refused to go through with the escape. (The Gendarmes wisely left him in the straight jacket until his ultimate release from the Bastille.)

First Phone Call

The first transcontinental telephone line was used in 1914. A person in New York successfully held a conversation with a person in San Francisco. Records don't show what the pair talked about. The only line heard was, "The check is in the mail."

Harry Hockmann seems to remember making a transcontinental telephone call back in 1904. Even though Hockmann is pushing one hundred years or more, his memory is quite remarkable. He says he remembers that phone call as though it were yesterday. (The touch tone phone, the area code, the direct distance dialing, the call forwarding... everything!)

UNUSUAL THEATERS

Theater of Dizzy Delights

Poogle's Theater of Dizzy Delights opened and closed one week in Los Angeles at the turn of the century. Harry says this amazing theater was ahead of its time and would probably do quite well with the youth of today, (if anyone could afford to build it). Poogle's theater featured several interesting lighting effects along the lines of today's laser and light shows. The whole production would build to a blackout at the finale and, during this time, the theater seats would start spinning around. When the lights came back on, the patrons would find themselves unexplainably dizzy.

The original theater was quite small and only had six spinning seats. Clyde Poogle wanted to build a chain of 2,000 seat theaters but he was never able to get enough backing from his investors. In a fit of despondency, Poogle strapped himself into one of his chairs and spun himself to death.

First Drive-ins

In 1933, the first "Drive-in Movie" opened in Camden, New Jersey. This accounts for the population explosion in 1934. Professor Hockmann was so impressed with the success of the drive-in movies, he immediately promoted the first "Drive-in Magic Show."

Hockmann found that his big stage illusions weren't effective when viewed through a windshield, so he started going from car to car doing close-up magic. After several black eyes, he decided to get out of the drive-in business.

Hypnotic Theater

The world's first "Hypnotic Theater" opened in 1924. This wasn't really a theater at all.It was an elaborate facade which looked like the typical vaudeville palace of the day. After buying a ticket and entering a grand outer lobby, the customer passed a doorman who, in actuality, was a lightning-fast hypnotist. From that point on, the spectator would think he was entering a huge and magnificent theater.

The stage show was unbelievable. It featured fantastic spectacles with horses, chariots, ice skating, etc. At the sound of a bell, the entire audience would wake up and find itself in a field behind the facade.

Palace Theater

"Hockmann, The Great" never played the Palace in New York. It seems Harry once made fun of the house booker of the Palace by yelling out his name in a tough pool hall in the Bowery. The house booker's name was Eddie Darling.

He did, however, headline the bill at Greasemeyer's Palace Theater in Clydewater, Utah. A split week at Greasemeyer's didn't pay well, but it did break the jump between Chicago and Portland. The beautiful old theater still stands but they turned the town into a parking lot.

KLOTZMEYER BIJOU

Hockmann is quick to point out that the New York Hippodrome was not the biggest theater in the world, as it claimed to be. According to Hockmann, the biggest theater was the old Klotzmeyer Bijou near Cicero, Kentucky.

The Klotzmeyer Bijou was built by Homer Holland, the designer of the Holland Tunnel in New York. It had the unusual feature of being only fourteen seats wide and seven miles long. People in the cheaper seats had to come with their own telescopes. The ushers used bicycles. There was no movie projector because they found the light petered out before it got to the screen. Harry Hockmann says he played the old "Klotz" many times in its heyday and even had a permanent reserved seat for his beloved wife, Maude ... in the 1,400th row, center. The Klotzmeyer Bijou was torn down in 1938 to make room for a new street.

ATLANTIS AQUATIC THEATER

Professor Hockmann's "Atlantis Aquatic Extravaganza of 1927" required a special theater filled with salt water. Hockmann rented the old Cheesham Theater in Brooklyn and had all the doors sealed. He had underwater lighting installed. The audience had to rent scuba equipment at the box office and enter the theater via a diving bell.

Hockmann's clever illusions were all switches on standard effects geared to a nautical theme. His sawing a woman in half, for instance, involved a saw-fish and a mermaid. One of his biggies was the Houdini needle swallowing trick using ordinary hooks. Another winner was his levitation and vanish of a great white shark (using the old "white art" principle). The show had a pretty good run, despite several leaks in the building. The Brooklyn Fire Department finally closed the water-filled theatre due to the lack of a proper fire sprinkler system.

Live All-News Theater

The first exclusive newsreel theater in the world opened at the Embassy Theater in New York City on September 2, 1929. Actually, the first all-news theater pre-dated the movies, according to Harry Hockmann. Back in 1880, the noted theatrical impresario, Augustus Hammerschlock, brought the "News of the Day" into his Hammerschlock Pleasure Pavilion in New York City. It was quite an interesting idea and might work today if there were more Hammerschlocks in the world.

Every week the Hammerschlock players would act out the news events from murders to battle scenes from wars and, at the end of each scene, the principals in the news item would come on stage for a bow. Hammerschlock became a victim of his own idea after an ax murderer he featured in a recreation went berserk, and chopped up the theater, (including Augustus).

First Duplex Theater

Railmeyere's Electric Theater in Twinbluff, Colorado probably is the first "Duplex Theater." It had a movie screen at one end and a live stage show at the other. Patrons could swivel their chairs in either direction and watch whatever entertainment suited them.

Professor Hockmann remembers the theater and said it was always a pleasure playing there because the performers could watch the movie while they were doing their acts. Sometimes, if the picture was really good, Hockmann'd play to 100% of the backs of the audience. If Mr. Railmeyere noticed this happening, he would give them less money, which he liked to call "back pay."

HOCKMANN ON VAUDEVILLE

Muscle Magic

Few people realize that Professor Hockmann started his career in Vaudeville as "Adonis, the Living Statue." As a youth, Hockmann had rippling muscles and enjoyed getting himself whitewashed in the nude every night. In later life, his ripples were in his bottle of Ripple wine, and he got plastered every night. Harry may be pushing the century mark, age wise, but he still has the body of a young man. If he can remember where the Irish Wake was, he'll try to give it back!

Harry was thrown out of the Vaudeville Artists of America Association in 1922. Hockmann had billed himself as "Hockmann, the World's Strongest Illusionist." This was strong competition in vaudeville for a strongman named Sandow. Hockmann might have gotten away with the billing since most of the other magicians of the day were rather small. Where Hockmann made his mistake was in the pictures he used for publicity. When Hockmann came up with the strongman concept, his agent, Homer Morris, told him to get some pictures retouched. Instead, Hockmann found a picture of a well-known vaudeville muscleman and had it retouched. Hockmann found one of the old pictures in his scrapbook and allowed it to be reprinted here. He still can't understand why the public wouldn't buy his little white lie.

Tent Show

Hockmann recalled some of the circus acts he has worked with over the years. "The Great Elasto" was a side show magician who had the rare talent of vanishing himself up his own sleeve! As far as tricky balancing acts are concerned, Hockmann would vote for "Madame Wonderknocker's Troupe of Human Yo-Yo's."

Although "Hockmann, The Great Magic Show" usually played the big vaudevillian houses of the day, Hockmann did one season under canvas. His big tent had a capacity of 4,000 people with upholstered theater seats and air conditioning. (Maude took me aside to explain the old Professor was slightly exaggerating on this. It seems the tent had a capacity for 4,000 people over the entire season. It held slightly under one hundred at any one given time. Also, she said, the seats were old apple boxes and the air conditioning only worked when Harry left his drink in front of their old electric fan.) Many circuses stopped using tents after the disastrous Ringling Circus fire in 1944. Hockmann's "Magic Circus" was a disaster long before that.

Rafto, The Great

Winthrop P. Thatchfelder headlined in vaudeville under the stage name of "The Great Rafto." He did an entire theme magic act with barehanded productions of inflatable life rafts and emergency flares. He was a sensation with seaport audiences from coast to coast to coast. At the end of his act, the stage would be covered with rubber boats. One night, the heat from the flares set off the fire sprinkler system at the old Bijou Opera House in Scranton, Pennsylvania. The audience had so much fun, the place was renamed the "Bijou Indoor Marina" and prospered for many years until it sprang a leak.

Badd Magic

Impresario Gustave Badd's flagship vaudeville house used to be where the Empire State Building now stands. Gustave Badd was famous in New York for having an eye for great talent. People would flock to see his theater to see his "Badd Acts."

There were Badd Singers, Badd Dancers, Badd Comedians, Badd Novelty Acts ... In fact, some of the greatest names in the business started out as "Badd Acts." No less a theater historian than Hockmann, Harry's friend George Burns, once lamented that "there is no place for a badd act to play anymore." Gustave Badd III is an amateur magician and is well-known for his own magical creations. "The Badd Move," "The Badd Card Trick," and "Badd Material."

Gustave's brother, August Badd teamed with Arthur P. Goode in 1923 for a season of split weeks under the name of "Goode and Badd." Goode was very good for Badd but the act did not get good notices which was very bad. Badd's bad habits included bad timing and bad manners, which was not good for Goode and Badd's bad act.

Fine & Dandy, The Two "Human Flies"

Once again, Hockmann has exposed the secret of two vaudeville artists who kept the audience baffled for years. Fine & Dandy always performed their human fly, ceiling-crawling act behind a glass curtain. Most of the audience didn't realize the curtain was a giant lens which made the performers appear upside-down. Actually, Fine & Dandy crawled around on the floor while the audience screamed in fear they might drop to their doom. (Their human fly technology was ahead of their time.)

Oolong Pekoe Tea Dancing

An old vaudeville act Hockmann worked with, on the Orpheum Circuit after World War I, was billed "Snappy Tea Tapping with Oolong Pekoe." As the orchestra went into an oriental version of George M. Cohan's "Over There" (the audiences were still very partial to patriotic songs in those days), Oolong Pekoe danced on stage with a huge silver tea ball cradled in her arms.

In a symbolic dance, Oolong would scatter the tea leaves on the stage and then do a shuffle-type dance on the tea leaves. The tea grinding between her oriental slipper and the stage would produce an unusual abrasive sound and the effect was quite startling. The topper to the act came when Oolong would finish her dance, sit cross-legged on the stage and do tea leaf readings for the entire audience. The introduction of the tea bag in the late twenties put an end to the otherwise brilliant career.

Pied Piper Exposed

The Pied Piper of Hamlin did his weird trick of charming the rats and mice out of the village and into the river. That was back in the year 1284. Hockmann says this was just a cheap magic trick. All the illustrations you see of the Pied Piper make him look like an elf, dancing through the streets of Hamlin playing a flute.

The truth, according to Harry Hockmann, is that the Pied Piper mastered the ancient art of disguising himself as a huge piece of cheese. He not only looked like cheese, he made noises like cheese and even smelled like very ripe cheese. The rats and mice, naturally, followed him to the Weser River where the Pied Piper jumped in and swam underwater to the opposite side. The reason the town fathers wouldn't pay the Pied Piper's fee was because no one would get within smelling distance of him for weeks after the event. That's when the Pied Piper got mad, dressed up like a huge lollipop and lured the kids of Hamlin to their doom. Hockmann, later, did a single in vaudeville as "The Pie-Eyed Piper" which won him a plaque at the Bellevue Hospital Alcoholic Ward.

Manfred's Musical Mules

One of the most popular acts in vaudeville was Fink's Mules. Everyone knew that mules were slow and stupid, so seeing highly trained mules performing tricks on the vaudeville stage sold tickets to the rather rural audiences of the day.

Professor Hockmann's favorite mule act was not Fink's Mules, but rather an act from Germany, Manfred's Musical Mules. The mules played musical bells and auto horns. One of the mules had an incredible talent of snorting a remarkable rendition of the wedding march, (which brought tears to the eyes of newlyweds and audiences). Most people did not know that one of the mules was actually two assistants in a very realistic mule costume, (that explains their ability to perform tricks that even Fink's Mules would never attempt). The act could have played forever, if one of the miles hadn't become emotionally and romantically involved with the actor in the rear end of the mule suit.

G-Arbage

A magician in vaudeville, billed himself as "G-Arbage and Company." According to Hockmann, he did a rather standard magic act using bits and pieces of fruit and vegetables. He'd perform acts like the "Cut and Restored Banana," "Bare-handed Zucchini Manipulation," "Passe-Passe Pineapples" and "The Floating Watermelon." He got the idea while doing a straight magic act at a rather rowdy produce convention in 1936. At the end of his act, the stage was covered with fruit and vegetables ... and a few rotten eggs. He figured this was a great way to avoid starvation during the big depression since he would invariably have more food on the stage at the end of the act than at the beginning.

Incredible Record Breakers

According to Hockmann, many old vaudevillians couldn't get work in vaudeville and turned to getting bookings as "record breakers." Hockmann remembers a few:

Von Bathhousen played the Blue Danube Waltz non-stop for three days on the wet edge of a wine glass.

Clyde "Buck" Longhorne broke the world's record for Flea Roping at the 10th Annual Flea & Tick Rodeo at the Los Angeles City Pound in 1972. He roped the champion bull-flea "Ol' Red Eye" in less than 8 seconds! Prior to that, the record had been "Big Slewflea" roped in 10 seconds in 1932.

In 1938, that famed oriental Fakir Mohammed Chin Tau set a new record by making non-stop love on a bed of nails in the middle of New York's Central Park. (He and his mate were later arrested for "Indecent Acupuncture.")

Odd Juggling Acts

Hockmann ran across an old Variety review of an act called the "Jugglenauts." The Jugglenauts were big headliners on the Gus Sun vaudeville circuit. They bounced bowling balls off each other's head. Harry says the other acts called them "The Jugglenuts" because the stunt had left them a bit on the "slow" side.

Another great juggling act that played the vaudeville circuits with Hockmann in the twenties was "Boffo, the Balancing Blacksmith." He did a great trick juggling a red-hot crowbar, a one hundred pound anvil, a horseshoe and a cow chip. (Boffo was well received in the sticks.)

The Barnsdorf Cats

One of the best novelty cat act in vaudeville was the amazing Barnsdorf Cats from Austria. This was the act that first introduced to America sleight-of-hand magic utilizing the natural talents of Siamese cats. Magicians talk of the way those cats could back-paw a card. Their other popular effects included "The Multiplying Yarn Balls" and "The Hindu Scratching Post Illusion." The Barnsdorf troupe of cats were not seen in vaudeville after 1926. (That was the year the show merged with the Googenhoofer Dobermans.)

UNUSUAL VARIETY ACTS

Each year, Harry invites his old friends from the days of vaudeville for a party at the Rancho. Inevitably, the conversation always rolls around to the old standard acts like "Fink's Mules" or "Swain's Cats and Rats." But Harry loves to recall some of the lesser known novelty acts of the early vaudeville circuits:

"The Knucklebusters" (a unique percussion combo that played all the joints)

"Clodmeyer's A Capella Flea Choir" (who later changed their name to "Clodmeyer's Tap Dancing Fleas" when the younger fleas' voices changed)

"Hector and his Musical Jackhammers" (with his big finish, "Concerto in Concrete")

"Lady Florentine and her Housebroken Pigeons of Peace"

"The Four Flying Lindberghs, the Wingless Flyers" (whose real name was "The Smith Brothers" but they changed it because Lindbergh was a salable name in the late twenties.)

"The Late Wolfgang Phang and his Musical Iguanas"

"Elmo, and His Whistling Cats"

"The Elmira Sisters - Artistry in Bubble Gum"

"The Five Flying Bananas"

"The Merry Wanitas, Dancing on Smoke"

Harry put those acts right up there with classics like "Charlene, and her Musical False Teeth," "Herman and Huck, the Lightning Chicken Plucker" and "Tex Alamo, the Trick Snake Spinner." Several years ago, Tex tried to get on the old Tonight Show with Johnny Carson. He blew his chance at the audition. Tex twirled a ten-foot rattlesnake over his head ala Will Rogers, then he threw the loop over Carson's head. It seems Johnny isn't all that fond of reptiles.

They were great acts, one and all. According to Hockmann, none of them made it to the Palace, but they all made it with each other. Some dance acts tried to do variations on the "Sand Dance." There was "Alphonso, the Tack Dancer" who would do the old soft-shoe on a sea of scattered carpet tacks.

Another act was "The Great Guisseppe, the Shock Dancer." He made a big production out of attaching an electrical cable to a large raised copper stage. Then he put on a copper headdress with another cable leading to an impressive high voltage transformer. The switch was thrown and Guisseppe went into a most amazing eccentric dance with sparks flying everywhere. The most amazing thing, according to Hockmann, was that Guisseppe never took a dance lesson in his life.

Every year the venerable theatrical club, "The Wing Players," paid tribute to many of vaudeville's greatest tap dancers. In 1930, Hockmann was there and recalled some of the fabulous tap dancers that shared the bill with him. Bill "Bojingles" Clabber created a sensation by dancing on the tip of a twenty foot flagpole. (He met an untimely demise when he forgot he was dancing on a flagpole and did a "touch-toe and splits".)

Another amazing dancing act, according to Hockmann, was "The Great Lightfoot," an Indian who tap danced with fresh ostrich eggs strapped to his moccasins. Then there was "Silent Slidmore" who did the world's quietest soft shoe routine, dancing barefoot on a bed of marshmallows and whipped cream. They were the best of the great novelty acts.

Sidney's Silly Seals

The first Christmas Seal was placed on sale in Wilmington, Delaware December 9, 1907. (Hockmann didn't have his hearing aid turned up when he was asked about Christmas Seals so his reply concerned a few unbelievable facts about one of vaudeville's little known seal acts.) "Sidney's Silly Seals" featured six seals and a sea lion. The sea lion acted as the emcee slapping his flippers together to bring on the seals for their individual specialty. Sally, the Seal Soprano, stopped the show nightly singing, "After the Ball" while other seals balanced beach balls on their noses. Most seal acts of the day played musical instruments but few people had ever seen a seal playing a harp. The grand finale of "Sidney's Silly Seals" found the entire company doing a takeoff of Mack Sennett's "Keystone Kops" silent comedies ... the sea lion's imitation of Charlie Chaplin was especially hilarious, using his flippers and with his tail he could throw three custard pies at a time.

Ant Shows

"The Chinese Trained Ant Wonder Show" opened at the Wong How Fung Music Hall in Shanghai in 1913. One of the big scenic effects of the Ant Show was a huge magnifying glass that was lowered in front of the ant arena, giving everyone a great view of the magic ants. All the ants were Chinese except one big red ant that was imported from Russia. The ants did pretty standard stuff like the "Sawing an Ant in Half," "Floating the Ant" and, of course, the famous "Hindu Ant Trick," wherein a length of thread is tossed in the air and becomes rigid. A little ant, wearing a turban, climbs to the top of the thread and then vanishes in a puff of Raid. Hockmann says this was a great show, but it never played the United States because of the strong-arm tactics of the Flea Circus Roustabout Union.

Artistry in Ants

In the golden days of vaudeville, quite a few great artists turned to strange and interesting acts in order to make a living. One of the best was Stuttgart Von Ratz who did an act called "Artistry in Living Ants."

The curtains rose to disclose a large ornate gold frame with a blank white canvas. Von Ratz entered wearing an artist's smock and beret.He carried a whip and an artist's pallet loaded with thousands of live, red and black ants.

At the crack of the tiny whip, the trained ants would leap from the pallet and go through a series of military maneuvers forming amazing scenes on the canvas. One portrait was Abe Lincoln with a moving beard. Another was the sinking of the Titanic. He closed with a patriotic red, white and black American flag waving in the breeze. Hockmann recalls that it took Von Ratz years to train the ants. It was a sensation! (Unfortunately, the act was totally wiped out in 1932 by a pest control man trying to rid the theater of cockroaches.)

Trained Flies

Harry tells of the magician who did a version of the classic dove act using trained dyed flies. The act went over pretty well until his dyed flies caught something from some house flies and then the dyed flies died.

Bird Acts

Harry started reminiscing about magic bird acts and recalled a couple of the most unusual ones. One act that played the Gus Sun circuit, out of Chicago, was "Branstoff's Baffling Buzzards." Wolfgang Branstoff would make his entrance center stage and immediately "shoot himself" with a blank pistol. Twelve giant buzzards flew in, circled above him and presented a sensational "claw and beak manipulation" act while picking at the seemingly lifeless form. Hockmann said it was a sensational, if somewhat, disgusting act.

Another bird act that came up was "The Great Shamdini" who billed himself as the cleanest bird act in town. He produced all of his pigeons upside-down. Hockmann had a dove act for a season or two. He will never forget the time he was booked into London's posh but very adult "Bim-Bam Saloon." The management said nudity was required in the act. It took Hockmann all day working with the pigeons ... plucking their feathers!

Invisible Menagerie

Mary Chase wrote a play in 1944 that won a Pulitzer Prize about an invisible rabbit named "Harvey." Hockmann claims Mary Chase stole the rabbit idea from him. Harry says the concept goes back to his "Hockmann's Traveling Magic Circus" which played in the midwest in the thirties during the Great Depression. In an effort to draw crowds without incurring a great deal of extra expense, Hockmann came up with the idea of an "Invisible Menagerie." The folks would pay fifty cents to go into an empty tent to see the invisible Chinese spotted pig, the invisible mammoth sloth, the invisible three-legged giraffe, and many other invisible animal curiosities ... including an invisible rabbit which happened to be six feet tall. Hockmann tried to sue Mary Chase for plagiarism but got as far as an estimate from his attorney. He also thought the publicity generated by his suit might revive some memory of certain warrants for his arrest in Nebraska.

Hockmann's Double

A rare photograph of Harry Hockmann's double. Hockmann claims he never used a double in any of his illusions and swears this picture was never taken. (The double is the one carrying the suitcases.)

Morris, The Merrie Mime

The difference between Morris and all the other mimes is that Morris really did have a glass box. He would go through the usual motions of trying to escape from the box. At the end, he kicked a hole in the glass using especially designed steel shoes.

Amateur Hour

The radio program "Major Bowes Amateur Hour" made its debut in 1938. Some of the great acts that made their first appearance on the Bowes Show included "Hee Yu, the Chinese Musical Merrymaker" who played "Chopsticks" on a set of tuned toothpicks. There was "Sam, the Inflatable Midget" who grew from thirty-six inches to six foot tall while playing a topical tune on the bicycle pump. The musical group "Six Hisses and a Missus" featured six trained musical rattlesnakes and a pretty young lady. The act failed because the Missus could never find anybody that could tune a rattlesnake. The winner of the first "Major Bowes Amateur Hour" show should have been "Fabulous Ferguson and his Musical Manhole Covers." Unfortunately, Ferguson died just prior to show time from a fatal hernia.

The Amazing Nudedini

Hockmann says "The Amazing Nudedini" came close to getting as much publicity as Houdini with his simple gimmick of escaping from a straight jacket, hanging upside-down from an aeroplane.

The gimmick was Nudedini wore absolutely no clothes underneath the straight jacket. The pilot was instructed to fly very low over the heads of the gawking spectators. The act was banned in Boston, but it was a big hit in San Francisco where hanging nude was more acceptable.

Hockmann swears that the writer of this book, Milt Larsen, piloted the plane for The Amazing Nudedini's final exhibition. On that day, the plane flew over the Golden Gate Bridge. (Unfortunately, The Great Nudedini flew *under* the bridge.)

ABOUT THE ARTIST

At a pre-publication party in the gaily decorated Hockmann barn, illustrator Paul Butler finally had the opportunity to meet the surreal sorcerer whom he had depicted for more years than he has been alive. Approaching the legendary wizard, whom he had so accurately represented in hundreds of drawings, Paul extended his hand while Milt Larsen announced, "Professor Hockmann, Paul Butler." Mistaking him for a busboy, Professor Hockmann thrust his empty martini glass into Paul's advancing hand while recollecting, "Paul Butler! Of course, I remember him well. The Ice Skating Magician of Hapsburg back in the 20's! He was great till he tried the fire act ... It's awful to see a magician drown on his own stage!"

"No!" Milt corrected, "Paul... *illustrator*?" Milt and Paul both sighed in relief as Hockmann corrected himself. "Oh! Paul Illustrator? I could have sworn you said, 'Butler'!" Before Milt could correct him again, the Professor began a forty minute tirade on Paul Illustrator, the psychic who worked the maiden voyage of the Titanic. He concluded with "It was probably best he didn't survive the tragedy because his career as a psychic was pretty much shot at that point."

Later that evening, the painting that graces the front cover of this book was unveiled for the first time. The product of countless hours of painstaking research and interviews, all who saw it were astounded by the fond memories it evoked. All except Maude, who broke into hysterical laughter upon viewing the painting, and screamed, "Oh, Lord! That never happened!"

Assured of the consummate detail that he strove to capture, illustrator Paul Butler asked Maude, "What do you mean? Everyone knows about the night Hockmann lost his pants."

"Oh, he dropped trou' at least once a week," Maude cackled, "but we *never* played to a full house like in the pitchur!"

As Paul allowed his head to sag between his shoulders, he started to walk out of the room a defeated man. That was when the Professor's voice rang out loud and clear, "Hey, Butler! Come over here!" Excited by his apparent recognition by the master, Paul lifted his head and raced to Hockmann's side, assured that he had finally come to his senses.

The professor handed him yet another empty martini glass and instructed, "And no olive this time, Butler!"

Maude Hockmann

Maude Hockmann appeared in most of the early Hockmann shows. Often she was billed as Fifi LaTour, which, Harry felt, lent an air of glamour to the show. (Note: *As the Publisher neared completion of this work, it was discovered there were no photographs of Maude. Hockmann was asked if he had any incredibly interesting photos of Maude. Harry went through his file and came up with this photo, which he claims shows Maude in one of her most provocative and innovative gowns. Maude says she doesn't remember the gown, the show, or the year. She also reminded Harry that she used to be a blonde, most of the time. As is the case with most of the facts in this book, we have to assume Harry Hockmann knows what he's talking about.)*